PREFACE

Engineering and building Bonneville Dam in the heart of the Columbia River Gorge proved a monumental task. The complex geology of the gorge combined with the great volume of the swift flowing Columbia to present many complex problems of site selection, proper construction techniques, and equipment design.

The project first received serious consideration in a 1931 Corps of Engineers' report to Congress. This study, the famous 308 Report, recommended constructing Bonneville Dam as part of a ten-dam effort to tap the enormous hydropower potential of the Columbia River. In addition, Bonneville and other proposed dams in the plan were to contain locks providing improved inland navigation. Depression-era politics drove the process leading to adoption of Bonneville project by the Federal Government.

Conceived as a way to quickly employ large numbers of unemployed laborers and engineers while producing long-term hydropower and navigation benefits, Bonneville Dam amply lived up to the hopes and dreams of its promoters and designers. In the short term, Bonneville supplied essential power for the Portland-area shipyards and aluminum plants that helped win World War II. After the war, Bonneville's power spurred a period of regional economic growth and opportunity. With the completion of a second powerhouse and construction of a new navigation lock, the Bonneville project continues as a vital part of the Northwest economy. Today's Bonneville Dam, named for an Army captain who had explored and described the Columbia River Basin and its resources over 100 years before the dam's construction, stands as a testament to his vision of the region's future greatness.

This book is dedicated to the thousands of men and women whose energy and commitment built this engineering marvel in the "wilderness" of the Columbia River Gorge. Bonneville Dam has repaid the original investment of dollars, imagination, and toil many times over through the continuing benefits of jobs and affordable living for the people of the Pacific Northwest.

CONTENTS

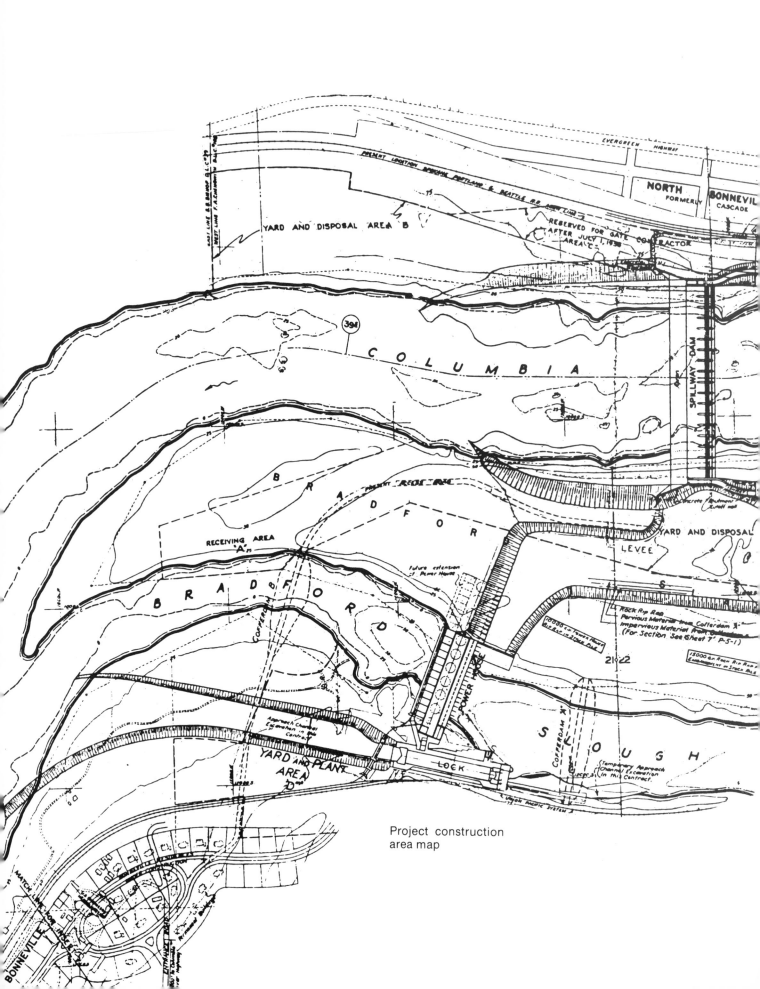

Project construction
area map

Chapter 1: Politics and Planning

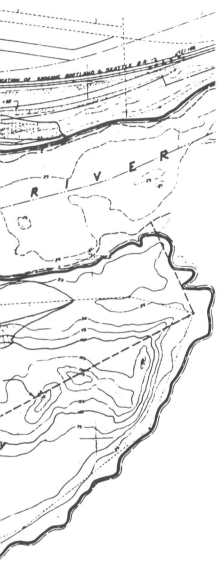

T he Federal Government's interest in building Bonneville Dam originated in a March 1925 Congressional directive to the Corps of Engineers recommending a study of navigable rivers across the nation "whereon power development appears feasible and practicable." The Corps was to formulate "general plans for the most effective improvement of such streams for the purposes of navigation . . . in combination with the most efficient development of the potential water power, the control of floods, and the needs of irrigation." In April 1926, the Corps submitted to Congress a list of rivers deserving intensive study. This report became the now famous House of Representatives Document 308. The Columbia River and its main tributaries figured prominently in the subsequent nationwide survey conducted under the provisions of House Document 308.[1]

Prior to Federal involvement in the multiple purpose development of the Columbia River, numerous state and local organizations attempted to generate interest in such development. These groups offered competing proposals for utilizing the river's potential, focusing primarily on the potential stimulus to either the region's agriculture or industry. The State of Washington, for example, sponsored surveys and promoted a major irrigation project in the Upper Columbia Basin during the 1920s. Oregon, on the other hand, emphasized harnessing the hydropower potential of the Columbia River and its major tributaries. In 1916, the Oregon State Engineer presented plans and estimates for constructing a series of projects in the river basin to generate power, improve navigation, and provide water for irrigation. The study, entitled *Oregon's Opportunity in National Preparedness,* admitted that no market existed for the enormous quantities of power such projects could produce. The report argued, however, that a market could be created by developing the manufacture of nitrates for munition in wartime while making fertilizers in peacetime. The report urged that "the most logical project . . . for early construction is at Bonneville, on the Columbia." In 1929, the Portland General Electric Company made borings and prepared preliminary plans for a dam in the vicinity of Bonneville. These plans, however, never proceeded because the estimated $30 million investment was too large an undertaking for the local financial market.[2]

THE 308 REPORT

Between 1927 and 1931, the Portland District of the Corps of Engineers labored mightily on the elements required for the comprehensive surveys called for in the 308 report. Until the summer of 1929, initial work on the survey consisted of defining the Congressional intent as to the scope and amount of detail to be covered in the comprehensive report and an estimate of the expense involved. Based on the preliminary planning effort, the Chief of Engineers authorized the additional work needed for the comprehensive report. The compilation of data required extensive field work involving foundation investigations, stream flow studies, topographic and hydrographic surveys, and reconnaissance of irrigable and flood-prone areas. The Corps then coordinated this information with investigations conducted for the survey by the United States Geological Survey, the Bureau of Reclamation, and various specialized consultants. The final report, containing 1,845 pages, first presented the data and cost estimates for proposed projects under four elements: navigation, power, irrigation, and flood control. The report then combined the four features into a comprehensive plan with recommendations for accomplishment.[3]

"while navigation possibilities sanction the report ... the power possibilities of the stream may be considered the basis of this report."

Col. Gustave R. Lukesh,
North Pacific Division
Engineer, 1927 to 1931,
and Portland District
Engineer, July 1927 to
July 1930.

In arriving at "the best plan of improvement for all purposes," engineering considerations remained secondary to the economic feasibility of the recommended projects. The North Pacific Division Engineer, Colonel Gustave Lukesh, made this point clear to his district engineers in Portland and Seattle:

> *Although a plan as a whole may be wholly feasible*
> *from an engineering construction point of view, or from*
> *the point of view of meeting the requirements as to full*
> *utilization of the river's resources and potentialities, yet,*
> *unless the plan is economically feasible, it can not be*
> *recommended.[4]*

The project justification contained in the 308 report reflected a real change from the 19th century rationale for Federal improvement of the Columbia River. While improved navigability of the Columbia River remained the reason for Federal expenditure, the test of public necessity had shifted. During the 19th century, Federal waterways improvements were justified if it could be argued that such work would result in the reduction of competing transportation rates and promote further regional development. By the 1920s, the weakness of such an argument became increasingly evident, especially since little or no freight actually moved on some waterways—as was the case with the Columbia above Portland at that time. As Colonel Lukesh noted, "the expenditure of funds . . . on river improvement for navigation whose only or main effect will be a reduction of rail or truck rates with the river failing to carry its quota of freight is a cumbersome and uneconomic procedure." He further noted that

> *there is no gain in national assets to offset Federal*
> *funds consumed in a river improvement that leaves the*
> *river unused for actual freight movement, though there*
> *may be a benefit to a fortunate section of the public. In*
> *determining the amount of contribution of Federal*
> *funds appropriate to a river improvement no credit*
> *should be taken for freight savings unless effected on*
> *freight actually moved on the waterway.[5]*

Structures built to improve navigability also had applications for power generation, and the Columbia long had been touted as a stream with vast power production possibilities. Thus, Lukesh could confidently assert that "while navigation possibilities sanction the report ... the power possibilities of the stream may be considered the basis of this report." Potential use of the Columbia for irrigation and flood control played a less important role in the Corps' proposed plan for comprehensive development of the river. Dam construction authority would rest chiefly on power development considerations.[6]

The Corps' 308 report recommended a ten-dam comprehensive plan for the Columbia River. It designated Grand Coulee as the key upriver project and Bonneville as the lowermost in the chain. Report data on the resources and industries of the Pacific Northwest soon became dated, as did the overly cautious analysis of future regional power usage. Nevertheless, the document's concise presentation on dam sites and structures formed the basic plan for Columbia River development over the succeeding 50 years.

In their review of the 308 report, the Board of Engineers for Rivers and Harbors generally concurred in its findings but urged development of the river's power potential by private interests, states, or municipalities. The Board stated that the Federal Government's contribution should be limited to the cost of the locks and channel improvements necessary to take advantage of the slack water navigation

Columbia River
Sternwheeler.

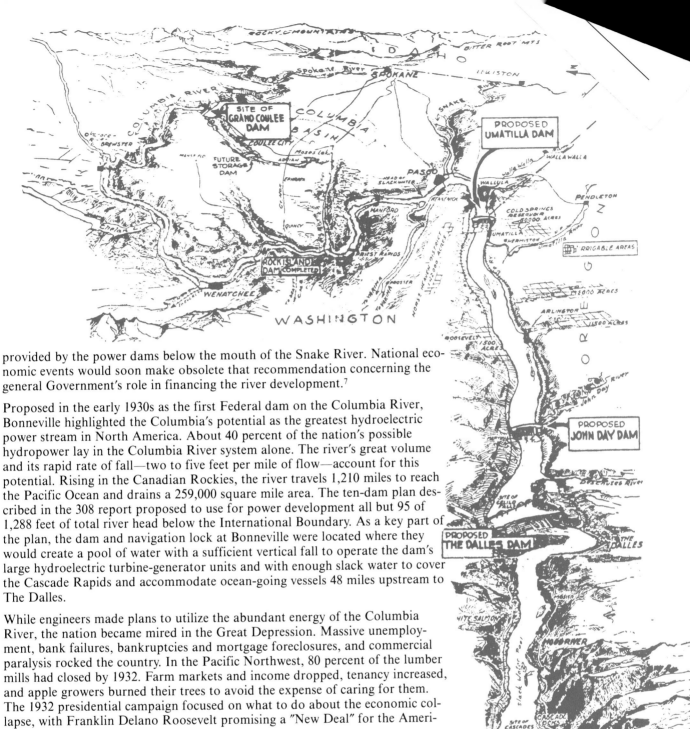

*Sunday Oregonian,
1 Oct. 1933.*

provided by the power dams below the mouth of the Snake River. National economic events would soon make obsolete that recommendation concerning the general Government's role in financing the river development.[7]

Proposed in the early 1930s as the first Federal dam on the Columbia River, Bonneville highlighted the Columbia's potential as the greatest hydroelectric power stream in North America. About 40 percent of the nation's possible hydropower lay in the Columbia River system alone. The river's great volume and its rapid rate of fall—two to five feet per mile of flow—account for this potential. Rising in the Canadian Rockies, the river travels 1,210 miles to reach the Pacific Ocean and drains a 259,000 square mile area. The ten-dam plan described in the 308 report proposed to use for power development all but 95 of 1,288 feet of total river head below the International Boundary. As a key part of the plan, the dam and navigation lock at Bonneville were located where they would create a pool of water with a sufficient vertical fall to operate the dam's large hydroelectric turbine-generator units and with enough slack water to cover the Cascade Rapids and accommodate ocean-going vessels 48 miles upstream to The Dalles.

While engineers made plans to utilize the abundant energy of the Columbia River, the nation became mired in the Great Depression. Massive unemployment, bank failures, bankruptcies and mortgage foreclosures, and commercial paralysis rocked the country. In the Pacific Northwest, 80 percent of the lumber mills had closed by 1932. Farm markets and income dropped, tenancy increased, and apple growers burned their trees to avoid the expense of caring for them. The 1932 presidential campaign focused on what to do about the economic collapse, with Franklin Delano Roosevelt promising a "New Deal" for the American people.

In September 1932, candidate Roosevelt spoke in Portland. He stated his interest in the "vast possibilities of power development on the Columbia River." He promised that if elected "the next hydroelectric development to be undertaken by the Federal Government must be on the Columbia River." Roosevelt personally visited, at that time, the general site of the future Bonneville Dam. While the election of Roosevelt and the clear public benefits to be gained from the Government investment in hydropower argued in favor of the Bonneville Dam project, other public works projects also competed for the limited funds available. Secretary of the Interior Harold Ickes opposed construction of Bonneville on the grounds that the Federal government could afford to build only one project in the Pacific Northwest and that one ought to be Grand Coulee.[8]

Only strenuous lobbying by Oregon Senator Charles McNary and Representative Charles Martin convinced the President to allocate the necessary funds in 1933. According to Martin, the President's initial enthusiasm for the project waned when questions arose about the adequacy of the foundation rock at War-

U.S. Representative Charles Martin
Oregon Historical Society
photo no. CN04879.

U.S. Senator Charles McNary
Oregon Historical Society
photo no. 14754.

Original Bonneville Dam layout.
Sunday Oregonian, 1 Oct. 1933.

rendale, the original site proposed for the dam. Roosevelt refused to commit Federal funds for Bonneville unless he could be guaranteed that a suitable foundation existed. Martin then secured an appropriation for the Corps to conduct the necessary geological surveys of the Columbia between Warrendale and Bonneville to locate a feasible site. Armed with a report from the Corps indicating that a suitable location existed at Bonneville, a few miles upstream from the Warrendale site, Martin and McNary extracted a firm commitment from the President to fund the Bonneville project. McNary later recalled about the final meeting on the matter that only "after much discussion and some urging, the President said he thought allocation funds might be made, but wanted us to see Secretary Ickes. This we did and later twenty million dollars was allocated for the commencement of the project." Amazed at Martin and McNary's success in overcoming intense opposition to Bonneville Dam within Roosevelt's inner circle, a Government official told Martin that he had missed his true calling: "You would have made a supersalesman."[9]

The exaggerated prose of Portland journalist Marshall N. Dana captured the hope and inspiration Oregonians felt in Roosevelt's commitment to build Bonneville Dam:

> *When President Roosevelt ordered the construction of the Bonneville Dam he marked the historic moment when the Government of the United States caught the vision of the West and began to make the dreams of its great personalities come true. Began to plant, too, the seeds of those regenerative activities and influences that help to keep governments virile and civilizations strong.*

Whatever the hopes and aspirations, without the timely completion of the necessary surveys, engineering studies, and economic justifications by the Corps of Engineers, local interests could not have successfully urged construction of the project.[10]

PROJECT AUTHORIZATION

The Federal Emergency Administration of Public Works authorized Bonneville Dam on 30 September 1933 as Federal Works Project No. 28, under provisions of the National Industrial Recovery Act. When work began on 17 November 1933, the plans called for locating a dam, a powerplant with two units, and a navigation lock in the vicinity of Bonneville, Oregon. The initial allotment contained $20,000,000 for construction, and $250,000 for preliminary study and design. Before Congress formally adopted the project on 30 August 1935, putting it under the regular appropriations process, $32.4 million in public works funds had been spent. It cost another $7.5 million to complete the undertaking as originally planned. Subsequently, the Corps installed eight additional power units to complete the project at a total cost by 1943 of $75 million.

SITE SELECTION

At the time of its authorization in 1933, plans for Bonneville Dam had not progressed beyond the preliminary study and investigation stage. The most vexing immediate problem involved selection of the exact site for Bonneville. Preliminary studies by various engineers between 1916 and 1933 had produced numerous possible sites over the seven-mile length of river stretching from Cascade

Rapids to Warrendale. The 308 report had recommended the Warrendale site, even though it consisted of unconsolidated sand and gravel. Uneasy with this choice, Congress ordered the Corps to review the data again. As stated earlier, additional borings and geological studies at the Bonneville and the head of the Cascade Rapids locations disclosed rock foundations, causing the engineers to reject the original Warrendale site. Further analysis indicated that the Bonneville site offered "the greatest advantages as to safety, navigation and cost." Based on this finding, Roosevelt approved the Bonneville Dam project.[11]

The complex geology of the Columbia River Gorge made site selection extremely difficult. Over the millennia, volcanism and a series of basaltic lava flows had created several geological formations through which the Columbia River cut its channel, creating a gorge over 6,000 feet deep. Even as shrinkage and folding created the Cascade Mountain Range, the Columbia managed to maintain its course, eroding a gorge over 200 feet deeper than the present channel. About 800 years ago, a massive landslide three miles in width and length, at Table Mountain on the Washington side, completely blocked the Columbia. The river eventually broke through around the southerly toe of the slide, forming the Cascade Rapids. Over a course of seven miles, from the head of the Cascade Rapids to Warrendale, the river fell 37 feet. Twenty-four feet of this drop occurred in the first turbulent 2,000 feet.

Bonneville Dam Record,
23 Dec. 1933

Boat Rock, site originally proposed for main dam spillway.

Geological instability also affected the south side of the river at this location. Along the Oregon shore the Ruckel landslide, extending two miles between the head of Cascade Rapids and Eagle Creek, resulted from continual ground movement where water flowed along the surface of the bedrock. Since backwater from a dam would saturate the toe of the slide and drown out the existing drainage tunnels constructed to stabilize railroad tracks, new work would be needed to restabilize the area. The consulting engineers and geologists determined that both the railroad and highway would require expensive and difficult relocation.

Finding bedrock beneath the slide debris proved a tricky operation. Supplemental core borings undertaken in 1932-33, however, disproved the earlier studies indicating that bedrock could not be found at suitable depths in the slide area. Additional core samples showed that bedrock at Bonneville and the head of the Cascade Rapids had gone undiscovered during the 1930 drilling because the con-

"I most certainly would not have recommended construction had I not been sure of the foundation for the dam."

tractor had not recovered whole cores nor distinguished the fragments of bed-rock from the overlying landslide debris.[12]

While the additional studies demonstrated the superiority of the Bonneville site in meeting the combined needs of navigation, power development, and low cost, the engineers had not determined the exact location of the main spillway dam, lock, and powerhouse. The first contract, let 17 November 1933 initiated work at the north end of Bradford Island at the "Boat Rock" site. A severe winter flood halted work on 25 December 1933, however, and further exploratory drilling disclosed more suitable foundation conditions about 2,000 feet downstream. In March 1934, the Corps abandoned the "Boat Rock" locale for the new location. At this spot, two basalt intrusions or uplifts in the bedrock provided ideal foundations for the dam, powerhouse, and lock. Upstream and downstream from these ledges, bedrock dropped off precipitously. The new location also meant a savings of $3 million and shortening of the construction time by one work season.[13]

Thorough surveys and investigations by the Corps of Engineers had proven the feasibility of siting a major dam, powerhouse, and navigation lock at the head of tidewater on the Columbia. Many, including President Roosevelt, had been

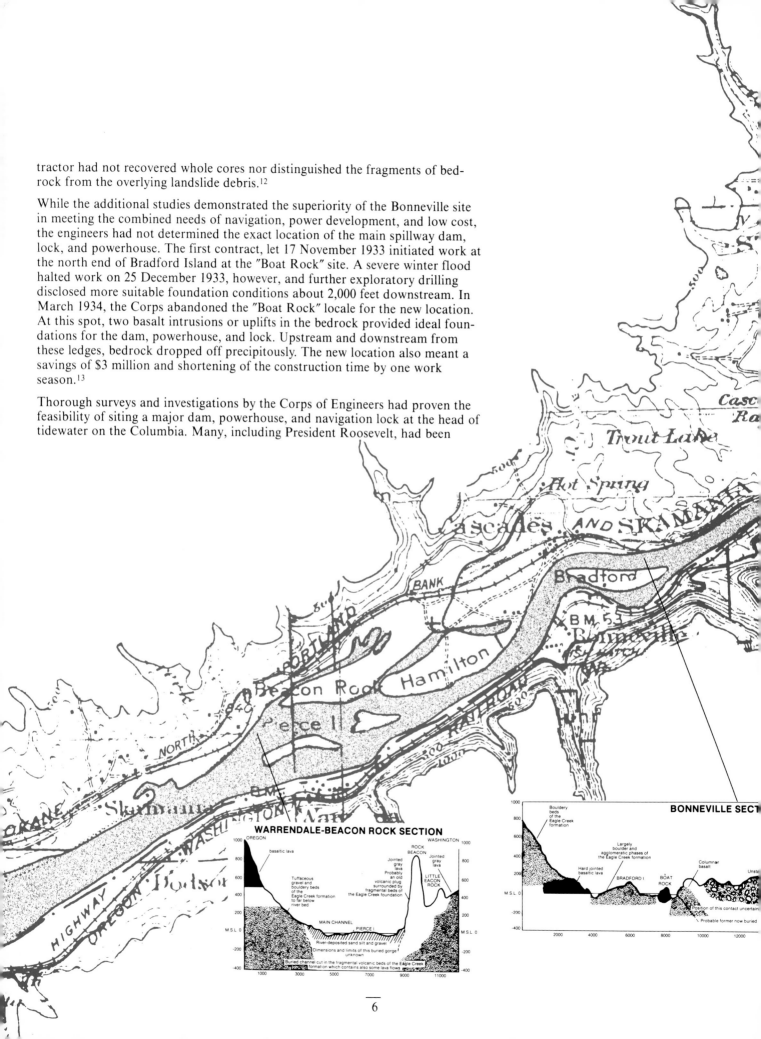

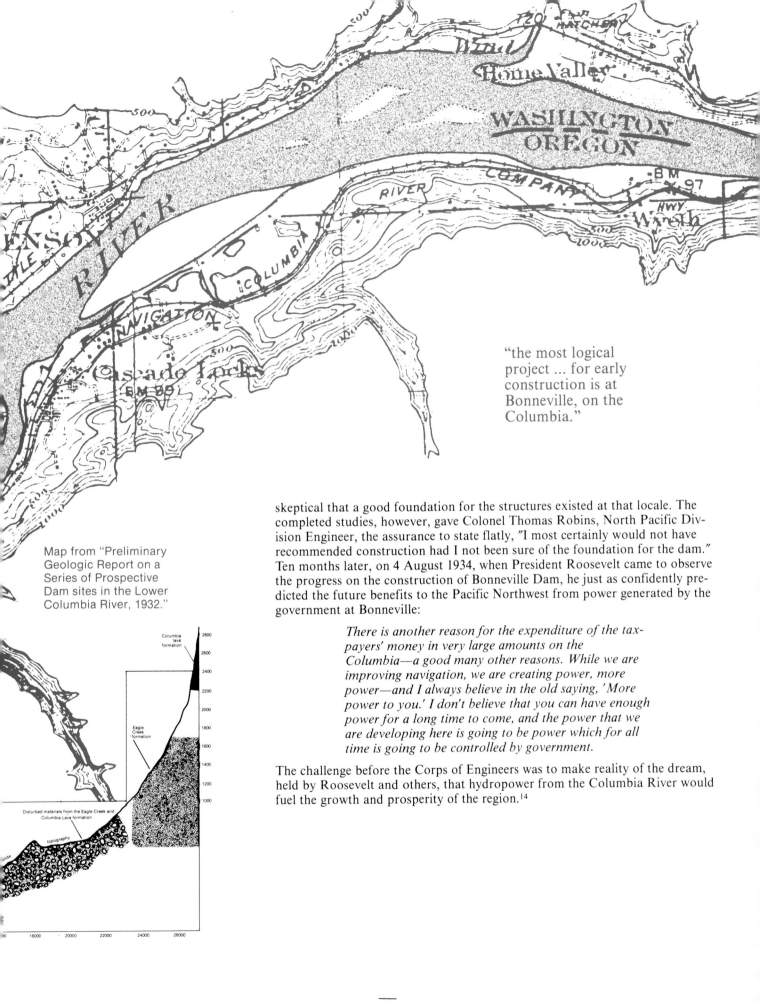

Map from "Preliminary Geologic Report on a Series of Prospective Dam sites in the Lower Columbia River, 1932."

"the most logical project ... for early construction is at Bonneville, on the Columbia."

skeptical that a good foundation for the structures existed at that locale. The completed studies, however, gave Colonel Thomas Robins, North Pacific Division Engineer, the assurance to state flatly, "I most certainly would not have recommended construction had I not been sure of the foundation for the dam." Ten months later, on 4 August 1934, when President Roosevelt came to observe the progress on the construction of Bonneville Dam, he just as confidently predicted the future benefits to the Pacific Northwest from power generated by the government at Bonneville:

> There is another reason for the expenditure of the tax-payers' money in very large amounts on the Columbia—a good many other reasons. While we are improving navigation, we are creating power, more power—and I always believe in the old saying, 'More power to you.' I don't believe that you can have enough power for a long time to come, and the power that we are developing here is going to be power which for all time is going to be controlled by government.

The challenge before the Corps of Engineers was to make reality of the dream, held by Roosevelt and others, that hydropower from the Columbia River would fuel the growth and prosperity of the region.[14]

Chapter 2:   Design and Construction

The design and construction of Bonneville Dam had to contend with a number of engineering challenges. Planning needed to accommodate the multiple purposes of power production, navigation, and migratory fish passage in separate structures built across two channels of the river separated by an island. The unusually large annual flood discharge of the Columbia River required using the entire main river channel for the spillway. Surveys and land acquisition for the project structures and reservoir flowage had to be carried out immediately. Excavation and construction had to be accomplished between high water periods, and complete diversion of the river was not feasible. Temporary fish passage facilities had to be provided for migratory fish. Since plans for the project had not advanced beyond the preliminary study and investigation stage at the time of initial authorization, design and construction proceeded almost simultaneously.

Since Bonneville Dam was originally promoted as a means to provide employment during the depths of the Great Depression, the Portland District Engineer acted quickly to get the project underway. After the Public Works Administration allotted the initial $250,000 for design and construction on 12 October 1933, the District Engineer recruited the personnel necessary to design the project. Several prominent engineers were hired as consultants to advise the existing district civilian engineering staff. D.C. Henry and L.C. Hill, advisors on the main dam and powerhouses, had consulted previously on the Boulder and Fort Peck dams. Other nationally-known consulting engineers with expertise on dam and hydropower design included John Hogan, L.F. Harza, F.H. Cothran, J.C. Stevens, and Raymond Davis. To analyze the complex geology and carry out the necessary foundation studies, the District brought in Professors Charles Berkey of Columbia University and Edwin Hodge of Oregon State College, well-known geologists. The major in-house staff included C.I. Grimm, chief engineer; Ben Torpen, senior construction engineer; H.G. Gerdes, C.G. Galbraith, R.E. McKenzie, and L.E. Kurtichanof as engineers in charge of dam, powerhouse, lock, and electrical design, respectively.[1]

To expedite employment on construction work, District Engineer C.F. Williams divided the work into a large number of contracts. As promptly as the project plans could be developed and assembled into discrete contracts, the Corps advertised and awarded each separately. Before contractors could excavate for the spillway, powerhouse, and navigation lock, the Government had to clear land, relocate railroad and highway routes, and construct a work camp. The Corps started construction of a 400-man camp with hired labor on 1 November 1933 and awarded the first relocation contracts on 17 November and 29 December 1933. The Corps issued the first principal contract, involving excavation for lock and powerhouse, 6 February 1934 for $8.9 million. Between the excavation contract and the main dam contract let on 12 June 1934, the Corps awarded seven miscellaneous contracts amounting to $1.2 million. The following month, the Corps accepted a $3.8 million bid for building the lock and powerhouse substructure. Other construction contracts awarded before the end of 1934 amounted to $.8 million. In addition to the first-year contract work, the Goverment hired a large force for non-contract labor. When the project was fully underway, the total work force averaged about 3,000, with skilled workers earning a minimum hourly wage of $1.20 and unskilled workers, $.50.

The Corps needed 800 acres of land below Cascade Locks for the main structures, sites for temporary and permanent buildings, railroad and highway relocations, construction work areas, and reservoir flowage. In addition, above Cascade Locks the reservoir pool would cover or periodically overflow another

A Scene
"Too Impressive
to be Told in
Every Day Language"

Cascades Canal and Locks, eventually downed out by Bonneville Dam.

52,000 acres. Surveying, appraising, and acquiring these lands proved a tedious and time consuming process. Since flowage affected approximately 70 square miles, the Corps had to run 700 miles of survey lines to make an official survey of the area. Ultimately, the Corps had to resort to condemnation to acquire all the property it needed.[2]

Pre-construct models of spillway.

DESIGN CHALLENGES

Building the spillway dam in a narrow channel passing a large flow presented complex hydraulic problems. To solve these issues, the Corps established a hydraulic laboratory and constructed a 1 to 36 scale model of three spillway gates and a 1 to 100 scale model of the river from the dam site to the head of the Cascade rapids. Initial studies focused on the best means of dissipating the energy of the flow over the spillway crest and on the dam's effects on backwater elevations. The object of the first study was to prevent erosion of the bedrock below the dam, and of the second, to limit flowage damage.[3]

Based on geologic and hydraulic studies, two main concerns governed the design of the spillway dam. The structure had to achieve stability on the comparatively weak foundation rock at the site, and it had to pass a large flood without causing a material rise in head water elevations during floods. The engineering design protected the sill against sliding and the effects of shear or scour by providing sufficient structural weight and by forming the foundation in large steps or

Close-up of spillway, piers, and baffle deck construction.

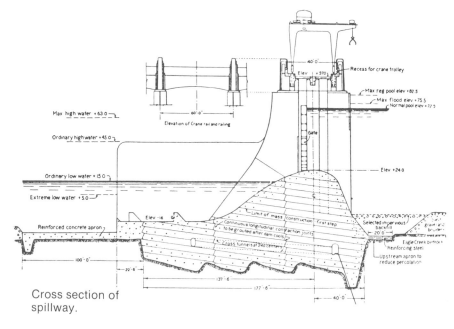

Cross section of spillway.

notches parallel with the lines of stress. To cope with the destructive power of the falling water from the spillway, the engineers placed a double row of reinforced concrete baffles on a specially designed overflow section on the deck and used a heavily reinforced, five-foot thick concrete apron extending 100 feet at the toe of the dam.

The engineers dealt with the wide variation in streamflow by using a relatively low sill and handling the overflow with exceptionally large steel gates set in deep slots between reinforced concrete piers. The piers were capable of withstanding large direct and side pressure from a combination of open and closed gates. To determine the optimum spillway gate size for handling anticipated flood flow, ice, and drift, the Corps' engineering team under H.G. Gerdes carefully studied other recently constructed dams, as well as Columbia River hydrology. Based on their analysis, the engineers decided that 50-foot wide gates, opening at two-foot intervals could safely handle regulation of the pool behind the dam.

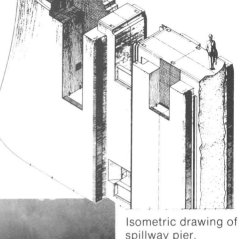

Isometric drawing of spillway pier.

Downstream side of south half of spillway dam as workers finish piers.

Spillway gate.

The engineers also sought a mechanical design which would provide safe, durable, and simple mechanisms for all gate operations. In the interest of economical construction and operation, the engineers designed each gate to be built in two parts at a foundry and then joined into single units at the dam for placement in the spillway slots. In operation, each gate moved on 26 enclosed roller-bearing wheels. Both the lifting and latching devices for operating the 200-ton gates were controlled from one of the two 350-ton gantry cranes. All mechanical designs developed by the engineers incorporated the latest advances in metallurgy, specifying stainless and nickel cast steel for load bearing and moving parts. In fabricating the gates, they required silicon steel for the horizontal girders and carbon steel for the skin plates and smaller bracing.

As built, the gravity concrete spillway dam reached 1,450 feet in overall length with eighteen, 50-foot wide gates. Twelve of the gates were 50 feet high and six were 60 feet. The base of the dam measured 132 feet and the height above the lowest point, 197 feet. The spillway design, placing 50-foot high gates on a low weir sill at elevation +24, created a normal pool elevation behind the dam of 72 feet above sea level with 2 feet of freeboard. When raised to their full open position, the spillway could pass a flood of 1.6 million cubic feet per second—37 percent greater than the maximum recorded flood of 1894. The gates and cranes cost $1.2 million.

Completed spillway.

To help the spillway pass large streamflows without raising historic flood elevations, the Corps increased channel capacity for three miles upstream by blasting and excavating obstructing rocks. In addition, the engineers widened the channel on both the Bradford Island and Washington shores at the dam axis, increasing the width from 800 to 1,200 feet by removing 954,293 cubic yards of material. Reinforced concrete cutoff walls at each abutment and reinforced concrete counterfort type upstream wing walls, along with downstream training walls, provided further safety for the spillway structure from the destructive forces of the river. Since the foundation rock was lower at the ends of the dam, the abutment

Panorama of Cascade Rapids area while rock blasting and removal is underway for navigation channel.

Blasting of boulder no. 8 for navigation channel at Cascade Rapids.

walls had to be built over 150 feet high. The Columbia Construction Company began work on the spillway dam in June 1934.[4]

Map of Upper Cascades of the Columbia River showing rocks to be removed.

The powerhouse, located near the lower end of Bradford Island to take advantage of an andesite foundation, originally provided for two hydroelectric generating units with substructure for four additional units. Excavated to a depth of 58 feet below sea level, the powerhouse initially was to house only two units and a station service unit; but even before these units began operation in March 1938, the Corps expanded the superstructure to accommodate four more units. As finished, the reinforced concrete powerhouse extended 1,027 feet in length and 190 feet in width and height (roof to bedrock). Piers 10 feet thick separated the units, forming initial intake openings 65 feet high and 62 feet wide. Each draft tube throat had a diameter of 23 feet and each turbine hub measured 8 feet. The initial two turbines carried a rating of 66,000 horsepower (h.p.) and the remainder, 74,000 h.p. The first two generating units produced 43,200 kilowatts (kw) each, while the remaining units were rated at 54,000 kw. The ultimate total output of this first powerhouse (518,400 kw) would have satisfied the electrical needs of a city three times as large as Portland in 1935.

The engineers based the general design of the powerhouse on the need to handle large quantities of water at comparatively low head. This required large intakes, concrete scroll cases, and deep draft tubes. Each generator was equipped with the Kaplan adjustable-blade propeller type of turbine. Engineers selected this kind of turbine because of space constraints at Bonneville and the wide seasonal variation of head at the powerhouse. The Kaplan turbine required less space per horsepower than other types of turbines and achieved maximum efficiency under a wide range of load and head. Twenty wicket gates on each unit let water into the turbine. An automatic governor on the units simultaneously adjusted the wicket gates and turbine blade angle to compensate for the variation in load. Each turbine unit weighed 900 tons and had a main shaft diameter of 40 inches. Each possessed a discharge capacity of 13,000 cubic feet of water per second— enough water to fill an average three-bedroom house. Vertical shaft type generators connected directly to the turbines and exciters which, in turn, were linked through a control station with the transformers on the upper deck of the power-

Completed generators.

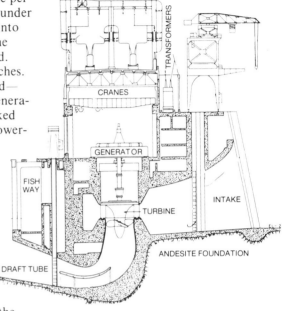

Cross section of powerhouse generating equipment.

house. The high tension switch yard equipment was located on the roof of the powerhouse.[5]

The electrical engineers worked under difficult circumstances, with the design and construction of the powerhouse structure occurring before the actual electrical load and means of meeting it had been determined. The engineers had to design a plant without knowing the precise type of equipment which would be used. Construction was pushed along at a frantic pace. According to at least one frustrated electrical engineer, "the only objective apparently being the dumping of yards of concrete and the placing of tons of steel. Structural design in the office was but a jump ahead of actual construction in the field."

Bradford Island served as the connecting link between the dam and powerhouse. The engineers, however, found it necessary to raise the height of this natural earthen dam by means of a 2,000-foot-long impervious levee and cutoff wall. Part of this wall was later removed when workers expanded the powerhouse to accommodate four additional units beyond the initial six. The contractor, Guy F. Atkinson Company, began excavation for the powerhouse and navigation lock under a single contract in February 1934.[6]

Several changes occurred in the navigation lock plans as they evolved. Preliminary designs called for a tandem lock with a short canal adjacent to the powerhouse along the Oregon shore. The dimensions of the lock chambers were set at 56 by 30 feet, sufficient for existing barge traffic. Soon, however, a combination of geology and politics produced changes in the original plans. The Chief of Engineers opposed construction of a ship lock on the grounds that current and potential commercial use did not justify the added cost. But on 28 December 1933, he gave in to political pressure and agreed to widen the lock chamber to 76 feet so that barges could be handled two abreast. Based on additional borings indicating that the andesite base at the lock could accommodate a single-lift structure, the Corps decided, in February 1934, to adopt a single lift design.

"Structural design in the office was but a jump ahead of actual construction in the field."

Excavation for main culvert and laterals in lock floor.

"the men handling the explosives became so clever that they could dress down the side of a wall as neatly as a stone mason working with tools."

While Roosevelt had backed the Chief of Engineers' finding against a ship lock at Bonneville, the President had agreed to reconsider at a later date if conditions changed. Local Northwest interests kept up the pressure to reverse his decision. In April 1934, Representative Charles Martin got the House River and Harbors Committee to authorize the Corps to study the feasibility of providing a 30-foot ship channel between the mouth of the Willamette River and Bonneville Dam. After prodding by Senator McNary, the Corps agreed to take another look at the feasibility and cost of constructing a ship lock. Based on this review, carried out in the summer of 1934, the Corps discovered that $2 million could be saved by building the ship lock initially, rather than barge locks which would be converted at a later date. When Roosevelt arrived at Bonneville on 3 August to view the progress on the project, he signalled his receptivity to a ship lock if justified by the Corps studies. To the welcoming throngs at the dam site, he clearly expressed his hope that "it will be found the part of wisdom to enlarge the locks at Bonneville so that sea-going ships may find practical passage up the Columbia as far as The Dalles." On 14 August 1934, the Secretary of War, bowing to the political pressure and the Corps' assurance that a ship lock was feasible, authorized construction of a single lift ship lock 76 feet wide, 500 feet long, and 24 feet deep over the sill at low water. These dimensions would accommodate 8,000-ton ocean-going vessels. Having a vertical lift of 60 feet made the Bonneville lock the highest single-lift lock built to that time.[7]

Excavation and rock trimming for lock and gate sill completed.

Workers scalping overburden and scaling down wall of lock.

The design called for excavating the lock chamber out of solid andesite rock and covering exposed wall surfaces with concrete anchored to the rock. The engineers conducted numerous model experiments before arriving at a system for filling and emptying the lock. The final design called for filling the lock by opening tainter valves located in the upstream end of the north wall. These valves connected with a culvert system beneath the lock floor which fed 41 floor ports. Water emptied through the same port and culvert system, which for drainage led to tainter valves near the lower end of the lock. The lower valves, in turn, discharged through floor ports downstream from the lower gates. Normal filling and emptying required 15 minutes.

Lock chamber near completion, showing filling and emptying ports in lock floor.

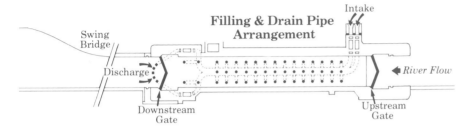

The electrically driven silicon steel miter gates at the upper end reached a height of 45 feet, while those at the lower end were 102 feet high—as tall as a 10-story building. The downstream gate leaves weighed 525 tons each. Emergency dock closure could be accomplished by lowering 13 steel bulkheads into recessed wall grooves. The plans called for all lock machinery to be electrically operated. An unusual feature of the navigation lock involved the use of six floating mooring bits in the lock walls. Designed by the Assistant Chief of Engineers, Brigadier General John Kingman, the floating fixtures enabled small craft to overcome difficult and dangerous moorings at low stages of the river. Finally, 500-foot-long concrete guide walls at each end of the lock enabled vessels to tie up while awaiting passage.[8]

Floating mooring bit installed in lock sidewall.

Lock and powerhouse structure completed.

PRE CONSTRUCTION: COFFERDAM AND EXCAVATION

The actual construction of the dam itself posed severe problems. The depth of water, current velocity, and harsh weather conditions together with the annual summer flood presented challenging conditions. The working season was effectively limited to an 8-month period from August to March. At the close of each working season, construction had to reach a stage permitting safe abandonment during high water. After extensive hydraulic studies, which also took into account the time and weather constraints, the engineers adopted massive timber cofferdams as the best means of diverting the river from the work site. Their plan called for dividing the river in half and unwatering each half successively. First, a horseshoe-shaped timber crib cofferdam enclosed the south half of the spillway section site. After the south spillway's partial construction during the 1935-36 low water season, the workers removed the cofferdam and the river flowed between the piers over the uncompleted crest sections while another cofferdam was put in place for work on the north section. Following completion of the entire north section during 1936-37, the contractors placed a prefabricated structural steel cofferdam over the crest section between the piers of the uncompleted south portion so that those units could be brought to final elevation. Workers finished the spillway dam, including gates and gantry cranes by June 1938. Each cofferdam consisted of three lines of cribs, forming an open "U" with shore arms diagonal to a river leg 460 feet long.

First step cofferdam completed.

First step cofferdam has been removed allowing river to flow through piers. Bulkhead is in place. Third stage has been overtopped by flood waters.

A unique feature of the crib cofferdam method of construction involved the need to "tailor" the crib bottoms to fit the irregularities of the riverbed. Since leveling

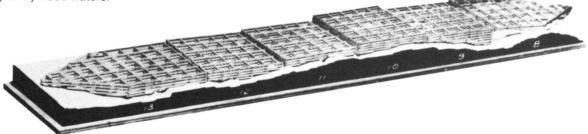

Model of cofferdam as it conforms to the river bottom.

the work site would have resulted in excessive cost and time loss, the engineers decided to dredge the thin boulder and gravel overburden and place the cofferdam directly on the exposed bedrock. After sounding on 2-foot centers and plotting the riverbed contours, the contractor carefully constructed the cribs to fit the bottom. Built of 12- by 12-inch timbers bolted together in horizontal courses, the 21 cribs generally measured 60 by 60 feet and reached up to 75 feet in height. The construction crews built the lower portions of the cribs on shore skidways and then floated them into position in the river. Laborers then completed the cribs to full height and sank them by dumping rock and impervious material into

Crib 13 under construction. Note irregularities of bottom.

Crib on skids ready to be launched.

their cavities. After filling, the cribs were decked to prevent erosion of the fill when overtopped by the annual freshet. Workers then placed a protecting wall of steel sheet piling on the river side of the cribs and blanketed the shore cribs with an impervious outside fill.

The job of designing, building, and placing these huge structures—each approximately as large as a six-story apartment building—in the 900-foot wide river channel with a depth of 20 to 50 feet of water flowing from 6 to 9 feet per second, severely tested the capabilities of the engineers and contractors. For example, the stress from the crib holding lines in a 9-foot per second current

Pile driving sheet steel cofferdam face.

Crib towed into positon for 2 nd step cofferdam.

Crib in position. Pockets being filled

approximated 300,000 pounds. To cope with the high current velocity, the engineers anchored the midstream line of the cofferdam directly on partly exposed bedrock near the center of the channel. The first cofferdam, though submerged by the annual flood of 1935, survived without suffering material damage. The Corps was less fortunate the following year when the annual flood partially washed out the second cofferdam. The contractors, concerned by the unusual size and potential cost of the cofferdams, refused to bid without plans. As designed by George Gerdes, chief engineer for the main dam, the cofferdams cost

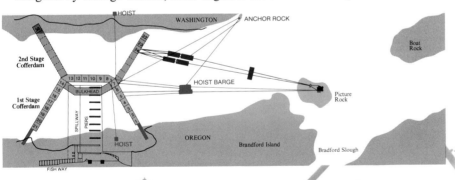

Diagram showing hoist arrangement for crib placement of cofferdam.

$2.5 million and consumed 8 million board feet of timber. At the time, it was the largest cofferdam job attempted on a United States river and attracted keen interest from the engineering community.[9]

Excavation for the powerhouse and navigation lock site followed a more traditional approach than required for the dam. In February 1934, the contractor commenced unwatering the entire work site by placing clay-faced earthfill dams,

Crib in place, resting on river bottom.

Panorama of Bonneville project with lock and original powerhouse nearly complete and spillway under construction.

one upstream and one downstream from the foundation area, and pumping out the water. The contractor located the pumping plant outside of and below the lowest points of the powerhouse and lock excavation, a great assist in keeping the work areas dry. Upon completion in March 1934 of the contract to temporarily relocate the railroad tracks occupying a portion of the lock site, workers began blasting rock for the lock chamber. After extensive blasting, the contractors removed 741,960 cubic yards of rock and debris from the powerhouse and lock site. The Corps and contractors used over one million pounds of explosives on the entire project, the largest volume in preparing the powerhouse foundation and navigation lock site. *The Bonneville Dam Chronicle* observed that "the men handling the explosives became so clever that they could dress down the side of a wall as neatly as a stone mason working with tools."[10]

Two pot holes located at powerhouse site, to be filled with concrete.

CONSTRUCTION

Work on the powerhouse substructure began 16 July 1934, the first concrete being placed in the foundation on 9 September. This initial concrete filled deep potholes extending 50 feet into the bedrock. The river created these holes during an earlier geologic era when it flowed directly over the area. Workers completed most of the lock chamber excavation during December 1934. Because of the depth involved, the contractor had to install a "More Trench" wellpoint system to dry up wet excavation areas at the east end. This drainage system consisted of deep set pipe wells located around the excavation area, intercepting the flow of groundwater and pumping it to the surface. By June 1935, when high water slowed work, about 55 percent of the lock and 90 percent of the powerhouse substructure had been finished. As the substructure neared completion in October 1935, the Corps let contracts to erect the powerhouse superstructure and to design and manufacture the turbines, generators, and other electrical components of the plant.[11]

Intake tube to turbine pit.

Upstream side of powerhouse substructure showing intake piers.

Construction of the powerhouse superstructure, awarded 31 October 1935 and carried out by the General Construction Co. and J.F. Shea Co., proceeded without disruption until the first two units went on line in May and July 1938. Increased power demands caused work to begin on four additional units in the fall of 1938. Two of these units came on line in December 1940 and January 1941. Expansion of the powerhouse foundation and superstructure for the final four units delayed installation of the last two of the initially-authorized power units. The delayed units went into operation in September 1941 and May 1942.

In the fall of 1939, rapidly escalating power needs had prompted the decision to extend the powerhouse to accommodate the final four units. This action had been authorized by Congress in August 1937 when it approved completion, maintenance, and operation of the Bonneville project by the Corps of Engineers. The powerhouse extension proved a difficult undertaking. Considerable over-burden and an earthfill dike connecting the structure with Bradford Island had to be removed and the extension carried out without disrupting power genera-tion. Plans called for earth and rockfill cofferdams which, once in place, proved less than watertight. At one point, work ceased for several days when a war shortage of parts caused water pumps to fail and allowed the site to flood. Major General Cecil Moore, then District Engineer, later recalled that "it was a great relief when they finally got the excavation done and the base foundation in down there because if that thing had gone out, well, then you would have lost . . . that whole powerplant." Workers completed the powerplant in 1943 and by December of that year the final unit went on line.[12]

Powerhouse tailrace.

Erection of one of 18-foot steel forms for concrete lining of Tooth Rock Tunnel.

Forms placed for pouring concrete lining of Tooth Rock Tunnel.

Reinforcing steel for Tanner Creek railroad viaduct.

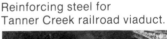

The location of the navigation lock and the size of the pool behind the dam required substantial railroad and highway relocation work. To lessen the extent of relocation and increase the safety of navigation in the channel three miles above the Bonneville Dam, the engineers blasted 118,600 cubic yards of material in the rocky areas of the Cascade Rapids. Removal of this material dropped the flood stage elevation, reducing the area inundated by the Bonneville project. Moreover, if left inplace, the rocky areas would have endangered navigation upon completion of the dam. Even with this and subsequent shore and channel work requiring removal of another 281,908 cubic yards of material, the engineers had to raise the Union Pacific Railroad track on the Oregon side 35 feet for a distance of 4 miles. On the Washington shore, the Corps had to move the Spokane, Portland and Seattle Railway 7 feet over a 5-mile-long grade. In addi-tion, sections of Washington State Highway 8 had to be moved to higher ground.

To accommodate the new Union Pacific line, the engineers built a 620-foot concrete-lined double track tunnel through Tooth Rock and a 900-foot double track earth-filled spandrel arch concrete bridge over Tanner Creek and the State Fish Hatchery grounds. In addition, the Corps had to devise a method for stabil-izing a troublesome slide area, known as Ruckel Slide, over which the railroad passed on the Oregon side. After extensive geological investigations by core drill-ing, test pit, and tunnelling, the Corps adopted the approach previously worked out by the railroad, but on a more extensive scale. Over a one-by two-mile area, the Corps located all water pockets and drilled several drainage tunnels to draw off the underground water flow that was causing land movement. The longest tunnel reached 2,200 feet back from the river's edge. To prevent the instability stemming from high-water erosion at the toe of the slide, the engineers placed a heavy blanket of riprap. The relocation measures, carried out during 1934 and 1935 at a cost of $5 million, proved effective.[13]

Tanner Creek railroad viaduct, awaiting installation of tracks.

The development of a ship lock at Bonneville Dam and a channel for ocean-going vessels from Portland to The Dalles required adjustments to two bridges in the Bonneville Dam pool. The toll bridge, popularly known as the "Bridge of the Gods," which crossed the river at Cascade Locks, and the Hood River-White Salmon Bridge upstream did not provide sufficient clearance for ocean vessels. To achieve the necessary headroom under the toll bridge, the Corps supervised strenghtening and extending the bridge piers so that the center section could be raised 44 feet. Workers accomplished this feat, using four 500-ton jacks. The project was completed by building new approaches on both sides of the Columbia. The Hood River Bridge renovation required a different solution, since raising the span proved uneconomical. After study, the Corps devised plans for installing a lift span to gain the needed 135-foot clearance at ordinary pool level. Reconstruction work on both bridges, funded by the Federal Government, came to $1.1 million.[14]

CONCRETE AND STRUCTURAL STEEL

Construction of the Bonneville Project involved placing about 1,000,000 cubic yards of concrete. To successfully accomplish this work, the Corps had to select, manufacture, and place a cement which would withstand the various structural and environmental forces to which it would be subjected. The design of the dam and the conditions of construction required a cement of special qualities. Since the ratio of the dam's base to height was large, producing low compressive stresses, the concrete did not need high strength. The structure, however, did require great tensile strength so that it could resist the cracking that stemmed from stresses generated by temperature changes within the hydrating concrete mass. Desiring to speed construction, the engineers planned to place the concrete in five-foot lifts, with three days between successive lifts. To permit removing the forms this quickly, the cement had to be capable of setting rapidly. Construction would be occurring under low temperatures (40 to 50 F), however, which would tend to retard hardening. Therefore, under the prevailing conditions, the concrete had to have a low ultimate heat of hydration but generate as much as possible of its total heat of hydration during the first three days to speed early hardening. To minimize volume changes due to heating and cooling, the cement mixture had to be as lean as possible without sacrificing strength or impermeability. Finally, to maintain homogeneity and resistance to weathering over time, the cement had to have low water gain and avoid segregation of the aggregate.[15]

Extensive tests of the chemical and physical properties of various cements by University of California consultants led them to recommend portland-pozzolan cement for the dam. Compared with the cements used to build Boulder and Norris dams, portland-pozzolan possessed improved workability, freedom from segregation and water gain, and a greater degree of impermeability. In addition, it had a more rapid rate of heat generation at early ages and less ultimate heat of hydration, greater tensile and compressive strength, and long continued gain in strength coupled with greater resistance to weathering and rough water action. At the time of its selection for the Bonneville Dam, builders had made little use of portland-pozzolan cement in mass-concrete construction in America. Many hydraulic structures in Europe had employed it with satisfactory results, however. Because of limited experience with portland-pozzolan, the consultants urged the Corps to develop precise specifications and implement a stringent testing program to assure the use of consistently high quality cement.[16]

Pouring concrete.

To carry out the consultants' advice, the Corps established a separate concrete division at the project to conduct laboratory testing, check the quality of materials and the design mixture, and inspect all operations connected with manufacturing and placing the concrete. Several steps comprised the actual mixing and laying of the concrete. Suppliers delivered cement by rail to the contractor's mix-

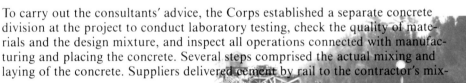

Aggregate plant showing main belt conveyor units and storage unit.

ing plants on the Washington shore and Bradford Island. Gravel aggregates for the lock and powerhouse cement came from the Willamette River, while sand and gravel deposits at Bingen and Rabbit Island on the Columbia River were mixed in the dam cement. To satisfy the different structural characteristics of the project, the concrete division ultimately developed several different mixtures, based on varying the aggregate size. The spillway dam required seven mixtures, while the powerhouse, navigation lock, and other structures needed fourteen blends. Corps inspectors carefully oversaw each stage of the process, including the preparation and blending of aggregates and the final batching and mixing process which produced the correct cement mixtures.[17]

Initially, the concreting gangs experienced numerous mechanical problems and management delays for several weeks before perfecting the pouring process. Inspectors, in the early construction period, criticized the excessive failures of concrete forms, "due mainly to improper design of forms and poor workmanship in erecting and anchoring them." Workmen constructed the spillway dam in blocks. They placed concrete in five-foot lifts, starting at the downstream apron and moving through the baffle deck, main dam, and upstream apron of each block of the structure. After placing forms and necessary reinforcement, laborers carefully cleaned the old concrete surface or rock foundation. The concrete gang then covered each lift with a one to two-inch layer of grout prior to dumping the main load of concrete. The grout consisted of cement and sand in the same mixture as the concrete, but without gravel.

Pouring concrete in powerhouse substructure.

The concrete crews, made up of 10 to 20 men, placed the concrete by bottom dump buckets of 8-cubic yards capacity. Two cableways rated at 25 tons capacity hauled these buckets to the point of placement. After dumping the concrete, the workers then used vibrators to puddle and compact the concrete into 18-inch thick layers until filling the form and bringing the lift to grade. The layer depth varied in reinforced sections, depending on the dimensions of the member and the amount of reinforcement and fittings in the form. The curing system consisted of garden hose sprays at 10 foot intervals over the area being cured. The sprays were connected to a pipeline conveying river water. To protect the fresh concrete from rain, the engineers developed a covering system consisting of 5- by 10-foot, light wooden frames, covered with canvas and supported 3 to 6 feet above the surface.[18]

Concrete curing with water spray.

Rain protection cover panels.

Although the engineers used different aggregate supplies, physical plant and cement (standard portland cement) to construct the powerhouse and lock, they employed mixing and placing methods similar to those used in the spillway dam. After the required cleaning and grouting of surface areas, concrete was transported to the work site by either cableway bottom-dump buckets or pumpcrete machines. Concrete gangs averaging 15 men placed the concrete in slumps of 2 to 4 inches, vibrated and then cured the lifts with hoses or a pipe spray system. The contractor experienced fewer form failures than in the spillway dam, even though special care was needed to keep the massive amount of reinforcing steel at least 2 inches from the form faces.[19]

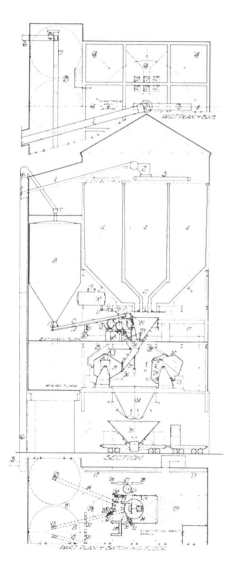

CENTRAL MIXING PLANT
MAIN SPILLWAY DAM BONNEVILLE

LEGEND

1. Belt Conveyor From Aggregate Plant Stock Bins.
2. Terminal Hopper & Agg Conv'r.
3. Reversible-Radial-Belt Conveyor Distributing Aggregate To Bins.
4. Nine Aggregate Bins For Sand & #1 2 3 4 Gravel-Approx. 200 c.y. Each.
5. Screw Conveyor From Cement Unloading Hopper.
6. Bucket Elevators-Dble Lift-Cement.
7. Screw Conveyor Distributing Cement To Silos.
8. Three Cement Storage Silos 2000 Bbls Capacity Each.
9. Water Supply From Tank & Heating Boiler.
10. Four 1500 Gal. Batching Water Tanks.
11. Water Lines -Tanks To Batchers.
12. Twelve Aggregate Batcher Charging Gates & Operating Units.
13. Four Rotary Cement Feeders.
14. Two Screw Conveyors For Fast Cement Batching.
15. Two Screw Conveyors For Slow Finish Cement Batching.
16. Two Water Batching Valves.
17. Electric Switch & Control Panels.
18. Operators Control Panel.
19. Two Each-Cement-Water-Accum-Aggregate Weighing Batchers.
20. Two Each-Cement-Water-Aggregate Adjustable Scale Beam Weight Controls.
21. Two Each-Cement-Water-Accum Aggregate Scale Dials With Limit Controls.
22. Six Materials Batch Wght Recorders.
23. Six Batcher Discharge Gates & Operating Units.
24. Two Batch Hoppers - Dry Materials.
25. Swivel Mixer Charging Coutes & Operating Units. Dry Materials. Two.
26. Closure Collars & Operating Units.
27. Swivel Water Charging Units. Two.
28. Two Pairs 4 c.y. Smith Tilting Mixers.
29. Electric Mixer Driving Units.
30. Mix Consistency Meters & Recorders.
31. Mix Timers & Meters.
32. Mixer Tilting Units.
33. Two Double Concrete Hopper Units.
34. Electric Dinkey Unit Transp To Cableways.

Impressive by daylight, the concreting process took on added drama at night. A newspaper reporter witnessed the operation in awe, describing the scene as "too impressive to be told in everyday language":

> *Lights everywhere, great floods of light that make an oasis of brilliance in the darkness of the night. In the background, dimly visible, black masses of the steadfast mountains, undisturbed by this noisy confusion made by puny men, moving like busy ants about the depths of the river's forsaken channel. Nearly 100 feet below sea level they (pour) tonight —monster buckets of concrete dangling from twin high lines, swiftly carried, carefully lowered to find the precise spot in the excavation for which they are intended. A bucket emptied of its 16-ton burden swings over to the north bank for a reload. As it descends a toy-like train runs out on its track to meet it. Swiftly a chute leaps out from the car, a cataract of concrete flows into the yawning bucket and . . . another contribution is on its way to the building of the Bonneville dam.[20]*

Powerhouse construction, night shift.

To ensure the highest standards in the required structural steel work, the Corps established a special inspection unit in September 1935. As one engineer noted, Bonneville Dam was not a leisurely "rivet tapping" job:

> *Tolerances are limited in certain instances to 0.01 inches in 5.0 ft. . . . Then, in order to expedite operations, it has been necessary to carry on construction simultaneously with design and detail.*

Since important structural connections were welded, the Resident Engineer decided to test all welders to establish a uniform quality of work. Even tools and equipment demanded special attention. Standard tools lacked sufficient precision, so that it became necessary to design special devices to control and coordinate all measuring tools. The 15 man inspection squad consisted of engineers and technicians expert in precision measurements and welding. They covered the dam site 24 hours a day and the powerhouse, 16.[21]

"it was a great relief when they finally got the excavation done and the base foundation in down there because if that thing had gone out, well, then you would have lost ... that whole powerplant."

Overview of construction showing reinforcing steel and concrete, south half of spillway.

THE WORK FORCE

To efficiently manage the complex and diverse tasks involved in building Bonneville Dam, the Portland District underwent reorganization. As a first step, the District established a five-man resident engineer's office at the dam site in October 1933. By December 1935, this office had grown to 21 people, overseeing contract work in progress, preparing quantity estimates for payments, and providing general engineering support. The growth in numbers of employees on the government payroll at Bonneville reflected the pace of dam construction:

1 November	1933	—	65
1 May	1934	—	285
1 November	1934	—	555
1 May	1935	—	580
1 January	1936	—	880

The first Resident Engineer had been a civilian, but in October 1934, Captain J. Gorlinski replaced him and Captain Colby Myers bcame Gorlinski's assistant as Administrative Officer. Gorlinski remained at Bonneville until his transfer to Washington, D.C., in May 1936.[22]

As construction went into full swing in May 1935, the Portland District split into two units. The First Portland District remained in Portland with jurisdiction over the Willamette and lower Columbia rivers and coastal projects, while the Second Portland District had responsibility for the Bonneville Dam construction, the Snake River Basin, and the Columbia River Basin between the mouth of the Snake River and Vancouver, Washington. In July 1937, the names of the units were changed to the Portland, Oregon, District, and the Bonneville, Oregon, District. In 1941 after completion of the dam, the Bonneville District reconsolidated with the Portland District.[23]

From left:
Williams
Grimm
Gorlinski.

First aid station for Bonneville project workers.

Temporary barracks for construction workers.

The Corps realized that the huge influx of laborers would overwhelm the limited housing available in the small rural communities in the vicinity of the work site. To meet this shortage, both the Government and major contractors built temporary accommodations for the large work force employed on the Bonneville project. By the end of January 1934, the Government camp consisted of a bath house, kitchen, main office, hospital, and six dormitories. Over the next year and a half, the camp expanded to include test laboratories, warehouses, miscellaneous shops, 17 dormitories, and enlarged mess and office facilities. The Government later took over 13 bunkhouses built for the contractor's use. All quarters measured 20 by 40 feet. At the peak of employment (spring 1935), the Corps put up nine, 10-man tent houses to supplement the previously built quarters. By

Corps of Engineers Bonneville Project Office.

One of twenty frame houses for permanent staff.

March 1934, the Government also had completed a 400-man camp for the contractor's force, consisting of 36 bunkhouses, 2 bath houses, and mess facilities.[24]

To provide living quarters for the permanent operating force, the Corps built a planned residential community on the Oregon shore west of the navigation lock and powerhouse. The buildings, designed by Portland architect Hollis Johnston in the colonial revival style and landscaped to enhance the beauty of that section of the Columbia River Gorge, consisted of twenty, two-story frame houses, an administrative building, and a recreation/auditorium structure. The site plan laid out the streets in a curvilinear pattern to fit the natural contour of the site and placed all water and sewer lines underground. In the spring of 1934, the Government work force dug the foundations, and private contractors completed the residences in November 1934 and the auditorium and administrative build-

Permanent quarters with Administration and Auditorium buildings complete. Later, brick structures were painted white to match colonial revival style homes.

ings in May 1935. After experiencing some weather delays, contractors completed the landscaping, utilities, and streets by June 1935. The total cost of the Government community came to $402,884.[25]

Labor employed on the Bonneville Dam project came chiefly from the relief rolls in Oregon and Washington, with a preference given to ex-servicemen in Skamania County, Washington, and Multnomah County, Oregon. The Corps apportioned the work force between Oregon and Washington based on the estimated percentage of project funding spent in each state. This formula allowed one Washington worker for every five Oregon hirees. To provide commercial services for the workers residing at or near the Government work site, the Corps built a structure to house a movie theater, grocery, drug and dry goods store, cafe, barbershop, and recreation hall. Private businesses leased the various concessions. The Government organized a police force, called the United States Guards, to protect property, maintain order, provide fire protection, direct traffic, and conduct public tours. The latter two duties proved the most onerous, as over 300,000 visitors thronged the work site prior to December 1935. Allowing the public to safely view a project of such magnitude without hindering the ongoing work challenged the ingenuity and tact of the guards. At the time of its organization, the U.S. Guards constituted the first Federal police force of its kind.[26]

U.S. Guards at Bonneville Dam project

BONNEVILLE DAM DEDICATED

The Corps accomplished closure of the spillway dam in September 1937. At this time, top civilian and military figures in the National Government formally dedicated Bonneville Dam. Before a large crowd and assembled dignitaries, President Roosevelt dedicated the dam to "a policy of the widest possible use of electricity," and to "more wealth, better living and greater happiness for our children." The contractor finished the navigation lock early in 1938 and by March of that year the first two generators produced power.[27]

The official opening of Bonneville Dam took place on 9 July 1938. The formal ceremony included such Corps officials as Major General Julian L. Schley, Chief of Engineers; Colonel John C. H. Lee, North Pacific Division Engineer; and District Engineer, Major Theron Weaver. Secretary of the Interior Harold L. Ickes threw the switch delivering electricity to the City of Cascade Locks, the first customer for Bonneville power. Great fanfare marked the passage of the first ship through the navigation locks in June 1938. When the water in the lock reached its full height, the crew of the *S.S. Charles L. Wheeler, Jr.* performed a flag ceremony on the deck of the ship. As the ship passed through the locks, the master of ceremonies proudly announced to the assembled crowd: "Ships are now passing through the heart of the Cascades Mountains and entering into the Inland Empire."[28]

Total construction cost of the project ultimately came to $83,000,000. Some had argued, at the time of construction, that investment in such a project would be a waste of money. As BPA administrator J.D. Ross noted to President Roosevelt in 1938, "there has been a tremendous propaganda trying to picture Bonneville and Coulee projects as white elephants." To the President, Ross confidently asserted that "the operation of Bonneville . . . is going to dispel the manufactured remarks of these crepe hangers." An article in the June 1937 issue of Collier's entitled "Dam of Doubt" claimed that there was no "real need for Bonneville," and that "there . . . [was] no market remotely in sight for the power" from Bonneville Dam. The article suggested the possibility of "fine concrete monuments scattered up and down the wilderness of the Columbia Gorge, still being paid for by the taxpayers." Events soon proved the critics incorrect.[29]

Ship lock dedication ceremonies, 10 July 1938.

"Ships are now passing through the heart of the Cascades Mountains and entering into the Inland Empire."

Roosevelt dedicating Bonneville Dam.

PHOTO ESSAY PAGES

Cofferdam Construction

The contractor unwatered the spillway dam site by means of a two-step cofferdam. After widening the river from 800 feet to 1,200 feet, workers constructed the first step U-shaped cofferdam of 21 cribs connected to shore by earth levees. Before constructing and placing the cribs, however, the contractor removed the river bottom overburden by a dipper dredge, determined the bedrock contour by sounding, and designed the cribs to fit the bottom. After erection, each crib was launched from inclined ways, floated into position, and sunk to bedrock.

Laborers placed the first crib, no. 13, on 3 December 1934 and completed the south cofferdam on 3 March 1935. After unwatering, workers cleared the foundation and constructed the south half of the spillway to elevation -8 and the piers to +45. To facilitate construction of the second step cofferdam enclosing the north half of the work site, the contractor placed a watertight bulkhead at the outer pier of the spillway's south section. Workmen then removed the upstream and downstream arms of the south cofferdam once they secured the bulkhead in place. While the river flowed through the uncompleted south half of the spillway, the contractor built the second step cofferdam between December 1935 and May 1936. Workers finalized the entire north half of the dam during construction season (1936-37). To complete the unfinished piers of the south half of the spillway, the engineers designed cofferdams to enclose successively one bay at a time.

The Crib Yard

Spillway Construction

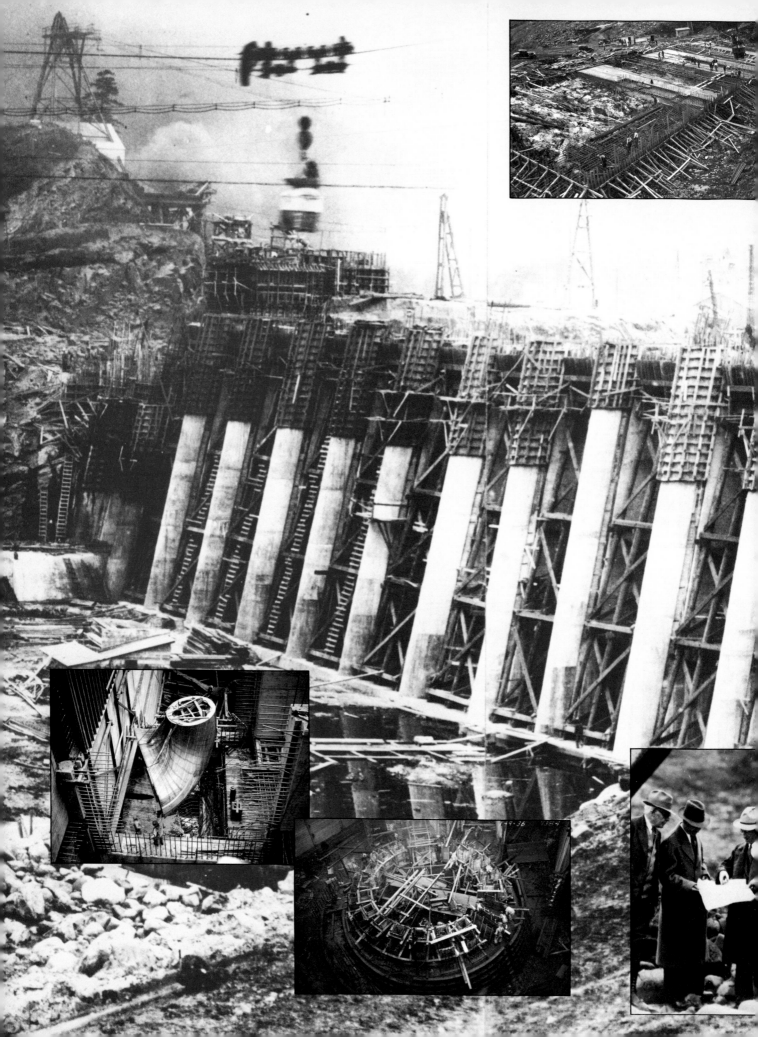

Powerhouse Construction

The Work: People and Equipment

Chapter 3: Hydroelectric Market and the War Effort

The Corps of Engineers' construction of Bonneville Dam and the Bureau of Reclamation's development of the huge irrigation and hydroelectric project at Grand Coulee made available vast amounts of Federally-produced hydroelectric energy. Long before these projects had been completed, distribution of their power became a controversial issue.

New Deal planners in the Pacific Northwest wanted a single agency, such as a Columbia Valley Authority, to generate, market, and transmit the electric power. Others preferred to separate the various functions among several agencies. In the case of Bonneville Dam, the latter interests wanted the Corps of Engineers to operate the dam and simply sell the project power at the generator bus to whomever would purchase it. Another, related, controversy swirled around the price to charge for the power. Colonel Robins, North Pacific Division Engineer, opposed a uniform rate for the sale of Bonneville power, arguing that it would drive up the average cost of power and thus discourage industry from locating in the region. Cheap power rates were seen as the region's best lure in the competition for electro-chemical, metallurgical, or pulp paper industries. In this same vein, the Portland Chamber of Commerce wanted a cheap rate for power as far as the Portland-Vancouver area to encourage industry to locate there but higher rates for greater transmission distances. People elsewhere in the region argued instead for a blanket or uniform rate, regardless of the distance from the dam. The latter group wanted the power distributed for maximum regional benefits.[1]

Since Oregon would be the main beneficiary of Bonneville electricity, the State was determined to have a major voice in any power pricing and distribution scheme eventually implemented. Beginning in 1935, the State set about formulating its position. In that year, the Oregon State Planning Board studied the cost of delivering wholesale Bonneville power to all substations in the State. The Board found, based on Corps-supplied data, that if costs were allocated on the relative distance of transmission, power in the Portland area would be available for $14.25 per kilowatt year. On the other hand, if costs were set as a single unit throughout the entire territory served, power in Portland would increase to $19.50 per kilowatt year.[2]

During 1936, the Planning Board developed a forecast of future power demands, indicating that Bonneville's generating capacity would be totally absorbed within nine years. With proper planning and marketing, the Board saw Bonneville power as a means to stimulate industrial development and end the state's colonial economic status. Oregon's economy, it stressed, depended heavily on raw material production and export, and on the import of manufactured goods. As the Planning Board put it:

> If Oregon continues as a state, producing chiefly raw materials, exploiting its land and mining its soils, its future will follow the same direction as its past. Its people will remain at the mercy of outside economic conditions, with their purchasing power dictated by prices prevailing for raw materials in world markets.[3]

The Planning Board sided with those in the State who hoped to induce the establishment near Bonneville of industries needing large quantities of cheap power. Accordingly, the Board recommended selling Bonneville power on a variable rather than blanket rate schedule. With great foresight, the Board also recog-

BPA's Ross substation at Vancouver, WA.

Colonel Thomas Robins, North Pacific Division Engineer.

nized the unique scenic and recreational values of the Columbia Gorge and urged the adoption of safeguards to prevent industrial development from irreparably damaging them.[4]

Governor Martin of Oregon strongly backed the findings of the Planning Board and their goal of using Bonneville power to promote the industrial development of the Portland area. Moreover, he recognized that, regardless of the ultimate pricing adopted, Oregon could not benefit from Bonneville power without timely construction of a transmission system. Accordingly, in April 1935, Martin urged the President to decide on transmission lines from the dam, so that the power could be utilized as soon as available. Oregon's powerful Senator Charles McNary, while sympathetic to the Portland area's economic concerns, defended domestic consumption of Bonneville power as its highest and best use. As minority leader and confidante of the President, McNary worked tirelessly with his Oregon constituents and Roosevelt's administration to craft legislation promoting broad and equitable regional access to Bonneville's electrical output.[5]

BONNEVILLE POWER ADMINISTRATION (BPA)

The Bonneville Project Act, guided through Congress by Senator McNary and signed by President Roosevelt in August 1937, settled the question of marketing Federal power in the Northwest. The Act assigned the Corps of Engineers responsibility for generating the power but rejected proposals simply to sell the power at the dam site to those able to come and get it. Instead, the legislation created a Federal marketing agency, the Bonneville Power Administration (BPA), to sell power in accord with the policy of "widest possible use of available electric energy." The law gave preference to publicly and cooperatively owned distribution systems. Roosevelt and McNary designed the terms and conditions of the sale of hydroelectricity by the BPA to prevent monopolization of this vital resource by limited groups. The performance of the Bonneville Power Administration would provide a "yardstick" by which the activities of other electric utility systems in the Pacific Northwest could be measured.[6]

Congress established the BPA as a bureau of the Interior Department. The BPA administrator was empowered to construct and operate necessary transmission and substation facilities and to enter into 20-year duration power contracts. The administrator also had authority to set rates consistent with the policy of the Act and sufficient to reimburse the United States Treasury for the costs of power generation and transmission facilities. Congress further ordered that the Federal Power Commission determine the cost allocations and approve rates. New Deal planners, however, did not consider this legislation the final word on regional power policy, for one clause stated that "the form of administration herein established for the Bonneville Project is intended to be provisional pending the establishment of a permanent administration for Bonneville and other projects in the Columbia River Basin." In 1940, the President issued an executive order giving BPA marketing responsibility for Grand Coulee power.[7]

Assembling stator for unit no. 2.

Under J.D. Ross, the first BPA administrator, the agency adopted a policy of a blanket or so-called "postage stamp" rate along the entire transmission system. This was done to encourage widespread development of natural resources and provide communities throughout the region full opportunity for economic development. The agency set the initial uniform wholesale price at $17.50 per kilowatt year —midway between the price based solely on the transmission distance and the blanket rate as identified by the Oregon State Planning Board. The demand for this cheap power grew quickly.[8]

BPA substation.

By the fall of 1938, work commenced to finish the powerhouse superstructure for four additional units. Even before their installation, the Corps had initiated in the fall of 1939 excavation and construction to complete the powerhouse by adding the final four units. These last units were rushed to completion in record time, beginning service in December 1943. At Bonneville Dam, and eventually at other Federal dams built in the Northwest, the Corps delivered electricity to the BPA at the converting facilities on the powerhouse. After Congress provided funds in May 1938, the BPA soon had a network of transmission lines radiating from Bonneville Dam. BPA completed its first high tension transmission lines, two 40-mile 230,000 volt circuits between the dam and the Portland metropolitan area, on 1 December 1939. Experiencing rapid wartime expansion, BPA integrated Bonneville power with that produced by other public and private power systems in the Northwest to become the chief supplier of electric power in the region.[9]

Alcoa aluminum plant at Vancouver, WA.

WORLD WAR II

Faded patches of camouflage paint still clinging to the Bonneville Auditorium and Administration buildings recall Bonneville Dam project's involvement in the war effort. The Army stationed almost 200 soldiers at Bonneville to protect railroad tracks and bridges in the area. In addition, the Bonneville project had its own guards. The Corps of Engineers posted guards in concrete "pill boxes" at the entrance to the project, by the Auditorium, and on the Washington side of the spillway. Neil Peer, who served as a wartime Bonneville Guard, later recalled that "there was a 50-caliber machine gun mounted inside the main powerhouse. They kept it trained on the front of the powerhouse door. A number of soldiers walked around inside the powerhouse, while the Coast Guard patrolled the river." The Corps even experimented with smoke screening the project by covering the area with dense clouds of partially burned diesel fuel.[10]

Power demand during World War II used all available capacity; indeed, occasionally the generators worked above their rated capacity. Power generated at Bonneville Dam proved crucial to the World War II military effort. That energy made possible the speedy development of three large aluminum plants in the Portland area, which produced material to fabricate 50,000 warplanes. Electricity from Bonneville also powered the shipyards at Portland and Vancouver, Washington. The yards at Portland turned out a Liberty Ship a day over an extended period. The shipyards in Portland drew on approximately 1,000 ship carpenters who had been trained at Bonneville in the skill of building the forms for the hull-shaped draft tubes. Power from Bonneville Dam also enabled the Hanford Engineering Works to produce plutonium for atomic bombs. Finally, the navigation lock at Bonneville also aided the war effort. At a time when railroad cars were in short supply, barges carried grain, ammunition, and other essential commodities through the Bonneville lock. Clearly, vital war operations would have been impossible without Bonneville.[11]

"there was a 50-caliber machine gun mounted inside the main powerhouse. They kept it trained on the front of the powerhouse door. A number of soldiers walked around inside the powerhouse, while the Coast Guard patrolled the river."

Smoke screen test during World War II.

Dam of Doubt

By Jim Marshall

Take a look at Bonneville. It's the $31,000,000 dam that turned out to cost $75,000,000. It's the first step in the government's scheme to turn the Columbia River gorge into a hive of industry. When completed the project will be five times as big as the TVA. And how about industry? Where is it coming from? That's what the sober Northwest wonders...

Bonneville Dam, key unit in the billion-dollar federal power project planned for the Columbia River.

"TH' GUV'MENT," said Mr. Ben Clark judicially, "says it's going to give us farmers around here cheap power from this dam. Sure, and why not? The private company'll give me all the cheap power I want. All I've got to do is plant about sixty poles and string three or four miles of wire to the plant and I can buy power for three or four mills a kilowatt-hour. 'Most any private company out here'll sell you juice for that, if you'll pay for the distribution from the bus bars."

We sat on the front porch of Mr. Clark's unpainted log house, two miles up a sloping narrow valley and a thousand feet above the swirling Columbia River, crashing through its 3,000-foot gorge. Down by the river a broad highway swept in curves along the Washington state shore. Across the stream, the Oregon hills rose dark and tree-covered. The wind spoke softly in the firs and pines and hemlocks back of Ben Clark's house. If you listened, you could hear the gurgle of falling water and the soft hum of spinning machinery.

"I've got a power plant, too," said Ben Clark. "Built it m'self. You want to see it?"

Fifty yards back of the house, where the valley narrowed, a rugged little dam of timber, rocks and earth held back the water in a pool. A few lengths of galvanized pipe led into a small stone building. Inside, the water rushed over a wheel. Through gearing, the wheel spun a generator. From the little plant, electric wires led to the house and the barn.

"Neat little rig," boasted Mr. Clark, squirting oil at it. "I ain't had any trouble with it and it costs hardly enough to count. 'Most any farmer can build one, if he's got a creek on his place, and most of them have, in these hills."

"The catch in a lot of these power schemes," said Ben, "is the distribution cost. I've got almost none—but if this plant was four miles away over in the next valley, it'd be worthless to me. Couldn't afford to plant poles and string wire and spend half my time maintaining the line."

We sat on the front porch again, looking out over the prune orchard that makes a living for Mr. Clark when the price of prunes is right and there is a good crop, which happens once in a while. Far below, lights twinkled in the twilight of the gorge. Down there, $75,000,000 of your money, transformed into steel and concrete, was finishing the building of Bonneville Dam. The dam, gray in the half-light, set out from the Washington shore, paused on an island near midstream and leaped for the Oregon cliffs on the far side. With a glass, you could see the elaborate lines of three fish ladders, designed to preserve the lower river's $10,000,000 salmon industry by allowing the fish to get upstream to their spawning grounds far in the Canadian Rockies. Toward the Oregon shore a long narrow rectangle marked the ship lock, through which it is hoped ocean carriers will steam forty miles up the river for freight.

Bonneville is the first and key dam of the Columbia River development scheme—which is about five times the size of the TVA project in the South. Second dam finished will be the Grand Coulee bar—a little $400,000,000 job to produce "power in the wilderness," described in Collier's by Walter Davenport in the fall of 1935. Present plans call for eight other dams; the final cost of the whole layout will be nearly a billion dollars. The estimates call for more than $700,000,000—and estimates are notoriously optimistic, as we shall see in a minute or two.

Geologically, the Columbia is one of our youngest rivers—a wild stream about twelve hundred miles long. It starts out in the Canadian Rockies and flows 450 miles through Canada before coming down to our side. In the United States, it drains an area about the size of New England. In this area live less than four million people. The first white man to see the river was Captain Robert Gray, who sailed in over the bar sixteen years after John Hancock so boldly scrawled his name to the Declaration, and named the river after his ship.

A Century Ahead?

From its entry into the United States, the river winds down through Washington state and then swings west to form the boundary between Washington and Oregon. From its mouth, 600 miles north of San Francisco Bay, it is more or less navigable for shallow-draft boats far into the interior. Tidewater ends at Bonneville, forty miles above Portland, Oregon. Portland, however, isn't on the Columbia, but a few miles up a tributary, the Willamette—which Easterners call the William-ette and Westerners the Wil-*lam*-ette.

Above Bonneville, the stream is beset by rapids and swift currents that make steamboating hazardous most of the time. In early days, before railroads came down both banks, there was considerable freighting on the river, but there is very little today. Millions of acres of Columbia River hinterland is just plain desert, productive if irrigated, worthless if not.

More than a quarter of all the potential—that is, undeveloped—water power in the United States is contained in the river's 750 miles of American course. Other streams in the basin contribute enough more to bring the total potential power up to two-fifths of the national reserve.

The Columbia scheme as a whole proposes to irrigate about two million acres in the Pacific Northwest; supply farms and factories with cheap power; carry away the products in ocean-going ships lifted and lowered through locks in the dams. But this picture, even the wildest enthusiasts admit, is a century ahead.

But even so, the whole project has been condemned by the National Grange and is bitterly attacked by Eastern and Midwestern congressmen. The Grange points out that practically all irrigation projects are far in the red; that tons of foodstuffs go to waste annually as it is. To the granger, the scheme looks like taxing him to subsidize amateur farmers to compete against him.

To the power man, the plan looks like piling on more power in an area which already has twice as much developed power as it can use and in which rates already are among the lowest in the country.

The Eastern complaint, apparently justified by figures, is against dumping hundreds of millions of tax dollars, mainly contributed by the East, into one remote corner of the country for the benefit, at present, of about one per cent of the people. Although, on paper, the various dams and projects will pay for themselves in a century or two, there is no certainty that they will not become enormous white elephants about as useful as the pyramids.

"Really," remarked Mr. Clark, rocking on the porch, "it ain't nothin' new. Every civilization, at some period—usually toward the end—goes in for monuments. Those old chaps over in Angkor built the biggest temples on earth. The Aztecs did the same thing. The Egyptians had to build the biggest pyramids ever. The Greeks and Romans were no better. Sometimes it makes me plumb tired figuring out the human labor that's been wasted in building the biggest things on earth.

"Every last one of these dams has to be superlative. Boulder's the highest. Fort Peck over in Montana is the biggest earth dam. Coulee's the goldarnedest chunk of concrete ever poured. They had a hard time figuring out a superlative for Bonneville, but they finally jiggered the plans to give 'em the biggest single-lift ship lock in civilization—if that means anything."

Bonneville got its start as a sort of accident. When Franklin D Roosevelt was campaigning in the West in the fall of 1932, he stopped at Portland, Oregon. In the morning he went to Gresham, a farm town twelve miles out, for a county fair speech. Then he came back to his Portland hotel and there was a press conference before lunch. Some of the local newspapermen asked Mr. Roosevelt the subject of his Portland speech. Mr. Roosevelt said he didn't quite know, and asked a secretary.

The secretary hunted around in the files and finally said he thought the speech was based on some old surveys of the power-producing possibilities of the Columbia River, made by Army engineers. Oh, yes, to be sure, said Mr. Roosevelt, that was it, boys. So, with the customary Roosevelt enthusiasm, the Columbia that afternoon was transformed into the world's greatest power producer, with industries booming everywhere and the desert blossoming for leagues around. Everybody cheered and Mr. Roosevelt boarded his special, with the secretary trying to figure out the subject of the next speech.

Pounding at the President

But if Mr. Roosevelt thought his power talk was just another speech, the go-getters in Oregon took it as a definite promise—and no foolin'. The old rivalry between the staid, sober Webfoot State and wild, rakish Washington to the north demanded action. Washington was going to get a few hundred millions for Grand Coulee and Oregon was after some of that easy money, too.

Of course, the Bonneville project is half in Washington and half in Oregon, but the Washington boys, having got their share—and more—handsomely agreed to let it be classed as an Oregon project—and hoped too many congressmen wouldn't study their maps of the Far Northwest. To most Eastern and Midwestern lawmakers the geography of that section is even hazier than are their economic ideas.

Because of what the Supreme Court might do to a government power project, Bonneville was designated a navigation scheme, just as Grand Coulee was called an irrigation scheme and other dams have been noted down as flood-control gadgets. The plans' sponsors hoped that congressmen wouldn't remember that in 1915 the government sank some millions into the Columbia at Celilo, a few miles above Bonneville, to build ship locks at the behest of enthusiasts who visioned ocean tramps sailing up into Idaho for wheat, fruit and lumber cargoes. It would be inconvenient if this were remembered, because to date only one ship ever has gone through the locks. The railroads down the river banks still haul the freight.

The locks will soon be forgotten, anyway. They'll be drowned out by Bonneville Dam's backwater—which, however, will not drown out the taxpayers' bill.

So, with the plan called a navigation scheme, and with the lure of easy spending money before them, Oregonians kept pounding at the President to okay Bonneville. In the van was the redoubtable Charles H. McNary, senior senator. At last, a few months after the 1933 inauguration, Mr. Roosevelt made his historic promise: "I'll go for $31,000,000, Charlie!"—and work got under way as a PWA project supervised by the Corps of Engineers of the Army.

Getting Free Front-Page Space

It was a triumph of political pressure and enabled Oregonians, passing Washington cars on the highway, to maintain their right of way and look their neighbor staters in the eye once more.

When Mr. Roosevelt said he'd go for $31,000,000 he didn't know the half of it. The present Army estimate is exactly $75,233,300 and going up every week or so.

While all this money flowing into Oregon is welcomed with open arms, hardly any intelligent people in Portland seem to believe in the dam. There is no market remotely in sight for the power and local concerns have enough excess capacity installed to care for normal growth for ten years or more. The best excuse Portlanders can think up for the biggest single-lift lock in the world is that the fact that ships *can* get up the river will serve as a brake against a rise in rail freight rates.

"Another thing I'm sick 'n' tired of hearing," said Ben Clark, charging his pipe and switching on the porch lights, "is this idea that if you have power and raw materials the wheels of industry'll start turning right away. Well, we've had power and raw materials out here for years—scads of both. The power companies and Seattle and Tacoma, that roll their own, would be tickled to death to give away, almost, their surplus power. The country's full of minerals and chemicals. But the factories haven't arrived."

"Why not, Ben?"

"Well, son, the first thing a factory has to have is somebody to buy its products. Power costs are only about one fifth of manufacturing costs, and getting a twenty-per-cent power rate cut means only a four-per-cent cut in the total cost. Say a factory moves out here—which is expensive—from New York or Connecticut or Massachusetts and saves four per cent. That doesn't help, because its mass markets are all back East and it loses its saving and more in added shipping costs. There's more buying power concentrated in New York City than in Oregon, Washington and Idaho combined.

"It's a fine dream," said Mr. Clark, looking out somberly across the moonsilvered river, "but it just ain't economic—yet. Maybe if we get twenty million more people out here . . ."

The cold figures on Bonneville are that when the first two units start spinning out power they will provide enough electricity to keep 150,000 flatirons hot. That's all. You could manufacture about 9,000 pounds of aluminum a day with the juice. Just what sort of a "huge pay roll" this would create nobody has figured out.

Incidentally, the investment in dam, locks and fish ladders works out at about $400 a flatiron, on this base.

For years, Northwesterners have been sold the idea that cheap power attracts industries. The thing has been chanted in every key from A-sharp to G-flat, despite the fact that for a score of years the section has had cheap power and been unable to sell more than half of it, even at almost give-away prices. In some favored sections you can buy power for industrial purposes at a mill a kilowatt-hour.

Building on the cheap-power legend, canny manufacturers all over the country have been getting free front-page space in all the newspapers of the Northwest, merely by buying a round-trip ticket to Seattle or Portland and telling reporters they were "surveying the country" for a new factory site. Variations on the "Blotz Bunk Factory May Locate Here" got onto page one almost daily.

Thus, hundreds of thousands of newspaper readers got a large dose of Blotz Bunk advertising at the total cost of a round trip for Mr. Blotz.

The catch in the government's cheap-power promises is that the consumer pays the delivery charges, which are six or seven times the cost of the power itself. You can get fish for nothing, too—all you have to do is hook onto them. Nearly all the cost of a fish in your refrigerator is delivery cost; almost all the dollars and cents on your electric bill represent the same item. Some power plants could give away the power at the bus bars and the bills wouldn't show enough monthly difference to buy a package of cigarettes.

Northwest politicians know this. In 1936 they made desperate efforts both in Oregon and Washington to get control of the distribution systems that must be built before any federal power is available to consumers. It would have meant splendid new political machines, with rafts of fat patronage jobs and all the meter readers, linemen, repairmen and installers working for the party in power. The idea was to float bond issues, string power lines and set up nice little electric empires in the statehouses at Salem in Oregon and Olympia in Washington.

After that, the rates could have been juggled around, or the profits used for any of a thousand and one political purposes—as gasoline-tax profits are being used here and there today.

But in both states the voters turned down the politicians by heavy majorities, apparently favoring distribution by the present private concerns or directly by the federal government. The latter scheme, with its inevitable duplication of existing power lines, isn't favored by federal engineers.

At Give-Away Prices

"You might figure it this way," says Ben Clark, sitting there on his porch in the moonlight, burning his own power, "the first settlers out here had to build the country from the ground up. The Lord left it awfully rough and unfinished and it wore out relays of homesteaders taming it. Fact is that fewer'n three per cent of the original homesteaders ever proved up. A homesteader'd do some clearing and run out of money and optimism and move on. This land I'm pruning has had thirteen owners since it was first homesteaded—and it isn't what an Easterner would call a finished farm, even now."

The wind whistling through the heavy timber up the valley gave point to his words.

"So the old plan," said Ben Clark, "was to get the people in and build the country afterward. Maybe all this dam and irrigation stuff is a reverse—build a country first and settle people on it afterward. Make it plumb easy for them—if they can make enough money to pay for the land and the improvement and the irrigation. I reckon I'm a right smart prune grower, but there's years when the price defeats me and years when the crop does th' same thing."

That's the question disturbing a lot of economic minds around the Pacific Northwest. It's fine to get new settlers, but it isn't so fine in a few years to discover they've gone broke trying to pay high prices for irrigated lands and high water charges with the proceeds from overproduced crops sold at give-away prices.

Hardly anyone in the Northwest says today there is a real need for Bonneville.

"But in a few years," they tell you, "there'll be population growth that will make it necessary. Some day, there won't be enough land or power. . . ."

Whether that's true or not, nobody knows. If it proves untrue, there will be some fine concrete monuments scattered up and down the wilderness of the Columbia gorge, still being paid for by taxpayers.

And here and there a graybeard politician will boast how he helped get half a billion dollars or more for a section that includes only 13 per cent of the national area and holds less than three per cent of the population.

"That's sumpin'," says Ben Clark, scraping back his chair and knocking out his pipe. "All the dreams may come true—but personally I've got my own private name for Bonneville.

"I call it the Dam of Doubt."

Chapter 4:

Fish Facilities

The Pacific Northwest is famous for its annual runs of salmon and steelhead trout. The Columbia River watershed historically produced more chinook salmon than any other river system in the world. These anadromous fish, which spawn in fresh water and grow to maturity in salt water, depend on the Columbia River system for their existence. The Corps of Engineers recognized at the time of its "308" studies that dams on the Columbia River posed a threat to the fish runs. The North Pacific Division Engineer, Colonel Lukesh, raised the issue with the Chief of Engineers in 1929:"In connection with tentative design of dams . . . it appears that provision should be made for the passage upstream of fish, especially salmon migrating to breeding places." He also accurately foresaw that "such provision may have an important effect upon the cost of the dam and possibly upon the water available for power generation during periods of low flow."[1]

The final 308 report, submitted in 1931, included fishways in its design and cost estimates for each proposed dam. However, fish passage facilities on the scale required for dams of the size proposed had never before been attempted. As the U.S. Commissioner of Fisheries reported to Congress, there had "never before been built, in either America or Europe, a structure of such size that obstructed migratory runs of such magnitude." Writing to Senator Charles McNary, the Commissioner promised "a detailed study of the character of the runs of fish at this point and the engineering features to be encountered in the construction of suitable fishways . . . in order to devise adequate protective works prior to the construction of the dam." Local fishing interests loudly echoed the Commissioner's fears that a dam at Bonneville would prove devastating, since it posed a barrier to the spawning grounds of 75 percent of the migratory fish runs. Under intense lobbying by Oregon fishing groups, Senator McNary pledged to "bend every effort to the end that adequate protection is afforded [the fishing industry]."[2]

STUDY, DESIGN AND POLITICS
Upon adoption of the Bonneville Dam project in September 1933, the Corps of Engineers immediately began work on fish passage facilities. Consulting with the U.S. Bureau of Fisheries, the fish and game commissions of Oregon and Washington, and various regional fishing associations, the Corps assembled a team of fisheries experts to devise a plan for passing migratory fish upstream and fingerlings downstream. Key members of the team included the Bureau of Fisheries aquatic biologist Harlan Holmes and hydraulic engineers Henry Blood and Milo Bell. Working under a compressed timeframe, the experts assembled existing data, conducted further studies, and debated the merits of various proposals with the interested governmental agencies and private fisheries groups. No consensus could be reached on the best type of fishway to use. Most Federal and Washington State fisheries experts favored fish lifts (or locks), but Oregon experts and commercial fishing interests believed that the lifts were too experimental and considered conventional ladders preferable at such an important location as Bonneville. The preliminary design submitted on 1 September 1934—less than a year after the project got underway—called for both lifts and ladders and a novel collection system.[3]

Harlan Holmes later praised the working atmosphere provided by the Corps, recalling that "from the very beginning our relations with the Corps of Engineers was extremely cordial and cooperative." The U.S. Bureau of Fisheries agreed with Holmes, noting that "throughout the study, valuable assistance was rendered by the Corps of Engineers in many details of design of the various structures required." Initially, the Oregon State Fish Commission was less complimentary of the Corps' Bonneville fish passage design. In response to the preliminary proposal, the Commission wrote to Colonel Robins "protesting against the adoption and installation of any untried or unproven device involving theoretical principles at Bonneville, which would in event of failure place the entire salmon run in jeopardy." Colonel Robins assured the Commission "that the War Department is very anxious to arrive at the best possible solution of this question of getting fish over the dam."[4]

North shore fish ladder and fisheries engineering laboratory.

Senator McNary, once again heavily involved in Bonneville matters, tried to reassure Oregon fish interests of the Corps' sincerity in finding the best solution to the fish passage problem. During the winter of 1934-35, McNary labored assiduously to bring all the parties into agreement on a fish protection plan. The Corps revised its plans to accommodate most of the Oregon fisheries' concerns, but in so doing increased the costs involved from an estimated $2.8 to $3.6 million. While the compromise plan was $900,000 less than what the Oregon Fisheries Commission proposed, it represented $1.1 million more than the Public Works Administration wanted to appropriate for fish passage facilities. After applying considerable political pressure, McNary extracted a commitment from the Public Works Administration to appropriate $3.2 million—enough to fund the key elements of the compromise plan.[5]

"there is no way of determining in advance whether or not the fish-protective works will be successful or how much, if any, adverse effects the dam will have upon the fish supply."

After an acceptable resolution of the Bonneville fisheries problem emerged in the spring of 1935, John Veatch, Chairman of the Oregon State Fish Commission, assured Senator McNary that "we are very well satisfied with the arrangements for the passage of fish at the Bonneville Dam." Veatch added that

> *Colonel Robins and his assistants at Portland have been at all times most courteous and have worked with us in every way possible. We certainly have no complaint as to the cooperation of the engineers and our work would have been made a great deal more difficult if the engineers had taken a different attitude toward our various requests.*

He concluded by acknowledging McNary's key role in producing a feasible fish passage plan: "Your efforts in our behalf in my opinion have been the chief factor in a satisfactory solution of our problems, have helped smooth the way for the engineers and have made our task much easier." As the Corps incorporated the elements of the fish passage plan into the actual construction of the dam, these features underwent further modification. The installed system—fish ladders, hydraulic fish lifts, a unique collection system, and bypasses—ultimately cost almost $7 million.[6]

FISHWAY DESIGN

The main feature of the fishways system constructed at Bonneville consisted of three reinforced concrete fish ladders. They resembled a long stairway comprised of pools 16 feet long, 40 feet wide, and 6 feet deep, each 1 foot higher than the last and leading to the 72-foot high pool behind the dam. Originally, the fish ladders contained solid overflow weirs, but the partitions were altered later to include underwater passageways. The submerged openings between the pools and regulated jets of water encouraged the fish to swim rather than jump from pool to pool, thereby avoiding injury. The plan required one ladder at each end of the spillway structure and one at the north end of the powerhouse.[7]

Internal view of fish ladder channel.

The fish lifts, one pair at either end of the spillway dam and another pair at the south end of the powerhouse, operated on the principle of navigation lock. Designed to accommodate 30,000 fish per day, the lifts were built and operated in pairs and consisted of a vertical hydraulic chamber 20 feet by 30 feet and 105 feet high. To attract fish into the chamber, a small amount of water was admitted and then allowed to flow out through the entrance. Once the fish swam in, the operators closed the chamber and raised the water to the reservoir level. A grillage rose beneath the fish to force them out at the top of the reservoir behind the dam. Initially, Holmes considered the locks superior to the ladders as passage devices, but over time the opposited proved true.

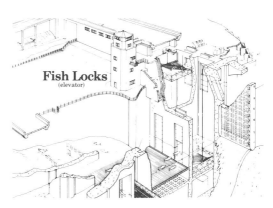

Diagram of fish lock operation.

The fish experts realized that the effectiveness of the fishway system depended in large measure on its ability to attract fish. Fishways at other North American dams had never satisfactorily solved this problem. After extensive model studies of the hydraulic features of the devices proposed and thorough analysis of existing data, Holmes recommended a collection system that provided "(1) an expanded or multiple entrance supplied with (2) a volume of water much greater than can be supplied through the fishway proper; [and] (3) the addition of this water in such a manner as to produce a nearly constant water velocity from the base of the fishway proper to the several entrances."[8]

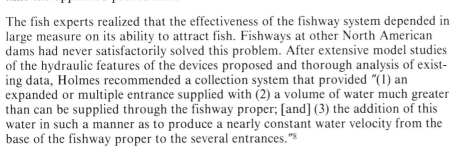

Main fish collection channel at first powerhouse.

As designed by the fisheries experts, the novel Bonneville Dam collection system consisted of two separate arrangements to serve the ladders and the lifts embedded in both the spillway and powerhouse structures. Across the face of the powerhouse, directly over the draft tube outlets, the engineers built a flume-like passage with openings where fish could enter along its entire length. This channel led to the fishway on the north end and to both the fish lock and navigation lock

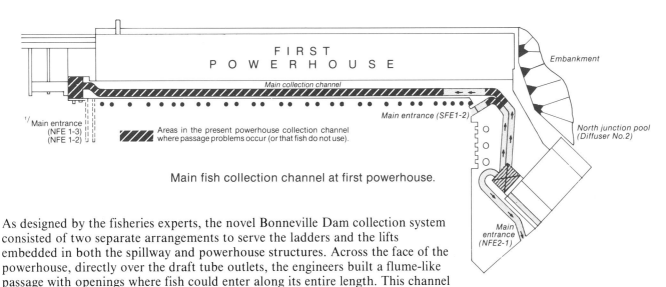

Dewatered fish collection channel at first powerhouse.

at the south side of the powerhouse. A series of diffusing chambers in the floor of the passage supplied auxiliary water at a controlled velocity to attract the fish. This augmented the flow of the fishway 10 to 15 times, the equivalent of a fair-sized river.

The spillway section used a different collection system. After considerable experimentation, the fisheries experts placed, in front of each endgate of the dam, passageways extending along the abutment walls from the ladders to the tailrace. At the downstream entrance, they used modified, conventional V-shaped collecting traps to prevent the fish from returning to the tailrace. The spillway collecting system received auxiliary water by the same method as the powerhouse system. An alternative fish passage, a series of long pools, and ladder sections designed chiefly for downstream migrants but available for upstream migrants as well, extended from the mouth of Tanner Creek for a half a mile to the upper pool near the east end of the navigation lock.

The fisheries' experts provided several methods to pass the downstream-migrating fingerlings. At the time, researchers believed that most fingerlings could safely make it through the turbines or the spillway gates when excess water was released. In addition, the engineers provided four special bypasses, three to

Vertical slot exit control section.

Flow guide walls.

Washington shore fish ladder under construction.

eight feet wide, at points where the fish were most likely to reach the dam. The bypasses, while similar to the ladders in design, were smaller and the drop between the pools greater.[9]

BONNEVILLE FISH HATCHERY

With the closing of the dam in January 1938, the public, engineers, and biologists anxiously awaited the spring salmon runs to test the $7 million fish collection and passage system. Prior to the dam closure in January 1938, the U.S. Bureau of Fisheries conceded that "there is no way of determining in advance whether or not the fish-protective works will be successful or how much, if any, adverse effects the dam will have upon the fish supply." The Bureau optimistically felt that the system would prove "that every possibility of failure or successful operation has been foreseen and provided for." The installation did not disappoint its designers. The fish readily found their way through the collecting channel and up the ladders to the reservoir behind the dam. Counting stations installed in each ladder served to monitor their operation. During the first 30 years of operation, the system passed one million fish of various species annually.[10]

Construction of the Bonneville Dam project also necessitated considerable redesign and relocation of the large fish hatchery facilities operated by the State of Oregon at Bonneville. Built in 1909 near the mouth of Tanner Creek, the Bonne-

Bonneville hatchery grounds during construction of Tanner Creek Viaduct.

ville hatchery (the largest in the world at the time of its construction) and rearing ponds soon played a major role in the propagation of Pacific Northwest salmon. The facility developed and retained a reputation as a world leader in salmon propagation and management.[11]

The Corps needed hatchery lands to accommodate relocation of the railroad and to provide a new access road to the Bonneville project. In all, the State transferred nearly 10 acres to the Federal Government and during 1935-1936 razed the existing facilities and constructed a new and expanded hatchery complex. The architects designed the buildings and grounds to compliment the architectural and landscape style of the adjacent Bonneville reservation. The Corps, for its part, acknowledged the presence of the hatchery in planning the railroad relocation. The simplest and least expensive right-of-way realignment required a 250-foot wide fill through the heart of the hatchery complex. To avoid this, the Corps proposed a 75-foot wide, 900-foot long earth-filled, spandrel arch viaduct. Eventually, the Federal Government acquired the hatchery grounds from the State, while the Oregon Fish Commission continued to operate and maintain the fish propagation facilities and programs.[12]

"we are very well satisfied with the arrangements for the passage of fish at the Bonneville Dam."

Recreational fishing at
Bonneville Dam.

FURTHER WORK NEEDED

Success of the Bonneville fish passage system emboldened supporters of the
Corps' 308 program for multiple-purpose development to vigorously push for its
completion. Between 1938 and 1975, the Corps of Engineers and public and private utility companies erected eight dams on the Columbia and seven on the
Snake. The fish passage facilities at Bonneville, supplemented by the results of
various studies, served as a model for the passage systems installed at these
dams. Over time it became evident, however, that fish passage structures alone
could not cope with the problems created by extensive hydroelectric development in the lower reaches of the two rivers. Studies revealed a 15 percent mortality rate from various injuries for migrating fish at Bonneville and other mainstem
dams.[13]

The Corps responded to the fish crisis on the Columbia with several programs. It
participated in the Columbia River Fishery Development Program, assuming a
major role in the hatchery mitigation effort. The Corps financed enlargement of
the main Oregon hatchery at Bonneville and supported various kinds of fishery
research into the problems of salmon culture. It focused special attention on the
difficulties downstream migrants faced. During their spring journey to the sea,
young salmon experienced heavy mortality from three sources: 1) passage of
juveniles through the turbines; 2) migration delays through the reservoirs; and 3)

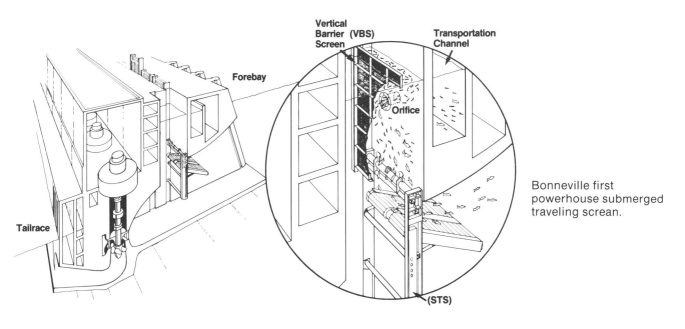

Bonneville first
powerhouse submerged
traveling screan.

gas bubble disease caused by nitrogen supersaturation of river water during periods of heavy spill.[14]

The Corps responded to the critical situation with several strategies. Experimentation led to structural modifications of spillways, including the use of deflectors
to reduce nitrogen supersaturation. Fish researchers developed methods to direct
the downstream-moving fish away from the turbines by constructing bypass systems using orifices, deflectors, and submersible traveling screens. They provided
additional protection by spill at dams without effective bypasses and, where possible, increased river flows to move fish through the reservoirs.

Concern over the potentially high reservoir mortalities of bypassed fish and the

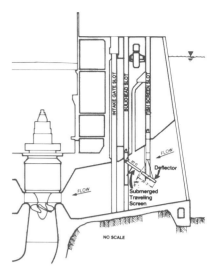

Detail of Bonneville second powerhouse submerged traveling screen.

great expense of bypass systems led the Corps to start another fish mitigation project in the 1970s. Since 1978, Corps personnel have annually collected juvenile salmon at the uppermost dams on the Snake River and at McNary Dam on the lower Columbia and transported them either by barge or truck around the downstream Columbia River dams to a release point below Bonneville Dam. During the 1986 transport season, the Corps team hauled 13,495,834 juvenile fish under this program. Research continues on refining the bypass and transportation systems. The most recent effort to enhance the survival of noncollected migrating juveniles involves the use of sophisticated electronic tools and sonar devices. With a goal of increasing safe fish passage while reducing losses in hydroelectric production and revenues, the Corps is testing sonar monitoring to direct spill patterns which stimulate fingerlings to pass through spillways and away from powerhouses.[15]

The Corps has attempted to incorporate much of this fishery research into the fish facilities at the second powerhouse. The structure contains fish ladders, a fish collection facility for tagging and monitoring adult fish, and a downstream finglerling bypass system. When ocean bound fingerlings reach the upstream face of the powerhouse, they are intercepted by thirty 28-foot wide by 23-foot long submerged traveling screens mounted in front of the turbine intakes at an incline of 55°. The screens direct the fingerlings into gatewells where they are discharged through 12-inch orifices into a 9-foot wide collection channel extending across the inside of the powerhouse upstream face. The collection channel transports the fingerlings into a discharge conduit with reduced flows of water. The fingerlings are released about 200 feet downstream of the powerhouse. Since the

Fish transportation barge

downstream facilities proved less effective than originally envisioned, they are still undergoing refinement. The fish facilities initially amounted to $82 million or about 12 percent of the total project cost.[16]

Since Bonneville Dam became operational in 1938, not only have additional dams been constructed in the Columbia River, but more power units have been installed at most projects. The increase of turbine units has reduced the amount of spill and provided additional peaking capability, passing more water and fish through the powerhouse where the fish risk greater mortality. Mitigation measures have helped reduce the impacts from more intensive management of the hydropower potential of the Columbia, but the cumulative fish mortality from the Columbia and Snake river dams remains high. The tradeoffs in the tug-of-war between the demands of power production and the needs of fish conservation, exemplified in the effort to improve fish passage at the Bonneville second powerhouse, continue challenging the Corps' fishery management program.

Chapter 5:

New Navigation Lock Second Powerhouse and

Since the Corps built Bonneville Dam in the 1930s, the Columbia River system has been developed into the largest hydroelectric energy producer in the world. The success of Bonneville and other multi-purpose dams in supplying low-cost electrical power attracted industries and people to the Pacific Northwest. The Pacific Northwest economy still depended largely upon timber and agriculture, but manufacturing became more diversified and service industries grew at a rapid pace. The region's aluminum industry, a product of cheap power and the wartime need to supply the aircraft industry, continued to grow in the post-war era. By 1975 it accounted for 30 percent of United States production, used 30 percent of the power available from BPA, and employed 12,000 workers. Energy-dependent aerospace and high-technology industries also developed during the post-war era. Farmers, too, used increasing quantities of electricity to supply the power needs of expanding irrigated agriculture. Cheap power encouraged the Northwest to indulge in the highest per capita power consumption in the United States. Reflecting this growth and opportunity, the combined population of Oregon and Washington increased by 73.5 percent between 1950 and 1980.

By the early 1960s, the ever-increasing demand for power in the region pointed out the limits of the existing Bonneville project. Based on its projections of regional energy needs, the Bonneville Power Administration requested, in 1965, that the Corps prepare a proposal for an additional powerhouse at Bonneville. The completion of upstream dams in Canada as well as Libby Dam in Montana and Dworshak Dam in Idaho had increased the low water stream flows in the Columbia River. The increased flows, especially during peaking releases at the upstream dams such as John Day and The Dalles, exceeded the existing generating capacity at Bonneville, with large volumes going over the spillway. A second powerhouse at Bonneville would capture energy lost through the spillway. The original Bonneville Act authorized additional power generation facilities when required by electrical demand.[1]

By the early 1970s, the Corps proposed a second powerhouse with eight main units and two smaller units, having a generating capacity of 558,000 kw. The need to limit tailwater fluctuations to support fish runs and maintain recreational use of the power determined the power plant capacity. Generating capacity represented the energy equivalent of 2.5 million barrels of oil or enough to meet the yearly power needs of 110,000 Northwest homes. As designed, the project represented a mammoth undertaking. The powerhouse, sited in a newly excavated river channel, measured 985 feet long, 221 feet wide and 210 feet deep. In all, the structure required 800,000 cubic yards of concrete and 70 million pounds of steel.[2]

STUDY AND DESIGN
After careful study, the engineers again chose the Kaplan adjustable blade propeller type of turbine. Compared to fixed blade turbines, the Kaplan had greater operating flexibility, higher overall efficiency, and improved fish passage capability. Eight of the ten turbines produced 105,000 h.p. at a 52-foot head and two, 20,700 h.p. at a 59-foot head. The main turbines, spaced 92 feet apart, had runner diameters of 330 inches and produced a discharge of 20,000 cubic feet per second. The power units' vertical shaft conventional generators carried a rating of 70,000 kV.[3]

Second powerhouse
under construction
within cofferdam.

The $245 million prime contract for powerhouse construction, awarded April 1978, constituted the largest contract to that time for a Corps' water resources project. The undertaking entailed a number of engineering challenges. The contractor, a joint venture of S. J. Groves and Sons, Peter Kiewit and Sons, and Granite Construction, had to remove enormous quantities of earth and rock: 8 million cubic yards for the foundation, 2 million for the forebay, and 13 million to form the tailrace. The excavation went 190 feet through debris deposited by a massive 800-year-old mountain slide. The 23 million cubic yards of excavation—enough to cover a football field 2.5 miles deep—were used as fill for the new North Bonneville townsite and additions to Hamilton Island downstream from the new town.

The Corps conducted over 80,000 feet of explorations consisting of test pits, wells, and core borings to determine subsurface conditions at the powerhouse site. The tests revealed a deep porous alluvium layer that allowed flows through it in excess of what a strictly pumping-dewatering system could handle. To keep water out of the newly dug powerhouse site, the Corps studied a number of

Aerial view of incomplete 2nd powerhouse.

Installation of generator units 2nd powerhouse.

Placing concrete foundation
for 2nd powerhouse.

options before deciding to erect a two-foot wide, one-mile long concrete seepage cutoff wall. Constructed in three segments in a 185-foot deep bentonite slurry trench, the cutoff wall reached elevation 80 on the river side and elevation 30 on the tailrace side. As the contractor gained experience in building the wall, he achieved significant cost reductions. The first segment of the wall cost $38 a square foot, while the third section required only $18 a square foot.

As in construction of the original powerhouse and spillway, the Corps used special concretes in building the second powerhouse. Since the foundation rock under the powerhouse proved susceptible to "slaking" or disintegration, it had to be protected from deterioration soon after being uncovered. The contractor successfully used roller compacted concrete to prevent deterioration of the exposed foundation rock. To provide protective cover for such rock on side slopes and smaller horizontal bench areas, the workers applied a three-inch thick layer of steel fiber reinforced shotcrete.

The design of the powerhouse interior called for leaving selected areas of unpainted concrete exposed to public view, requiring a concrete that yielded a relatively smooth surface, free of excessive cracking and other visible defects. To achieve this goal, the contractor used a mix containing a reduced water content.

As a timesaving measure during the conventional grout lift operations, the contractor proposed using shotcrete to embed the intake and tailrace bulkhead guides. Tests indicated that latex modified shotcrete possessed the best durability characteristics while exceeding the compressive strength requirements of the job. Because the latex modified shotcrete required only 24 hours of moist cure before air dry curing, the contractor shaved two weeks from the powerhouse construction schedule.[4]

RELOCATIONS: HIGHWAY, RAILROAD AND N. BONNEVILLE

Since the town of North Bonneville lay directly on the site of the new powerhouse, the Corps became involved in a controversial seven-year effort to relocate the entire community. Initial discussions between the Portland District and the town officials clarified the community's desire to reestablish itself at a new site. The town officials displayed enthusiasm for creating a model community, but such eager optimism soon dissolved as residents became aware of existing limitations in Federal law governing relocation.

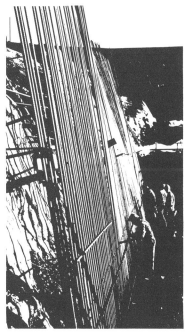

Placing steel reinforcement

New town of North Bonneville.

Federal resettlement authority, established in the Relocation Assistance Act of 1970, limited the Corps to dealing with individuals, not local governments. This fact stymied the Corps' efforts to accommodate, in any planned manner, the desire of most North Bonneville inhabitants to remain together in a new site. To resolve this impasse, Representative Mike McCormack of Washington secured a provision in the Water Resources Act of 1974 authorizing the Corps to directly assist government officials of North Bonneville in planning a new town, in acting as a real estate broker for lands in the new town, and in building utilities for its residents. Under subsequent agreements, the Corps promised that homeowners and businesses would receive compensation for their property and the opportunity to relocate in the new town at fair market value. The government also provided rent-free interim housing to those dislocated before lots became available in the new town. Finally, the government agreed to replace municipal facilities in the new location at no cost to the town. The Corps' relocation effort marked the first expenditure of Federal funds to plan, design, and develop a new community in connection with a water resources project.

From March 1974, when the first public meeting to choose the site for the new North Bonneville was held, to March 1978, when the Corps gave possession to the town, the entire process was filled with disagreement and acrimonious law suits. Throughout the controversy, the people of North Bonneville maintained a different view of the government's obligations in relocating the town than did the

Corps. The Corps had never before assisted in planning the relocation of a town as a whole and narrowly interpreted its legal obligations throughout the undertaking. On the other hand, the townspeople continually expected more financial compensation for the negative impact of the process of powerhouse construction and town relocation than the assistance legislation allowed. The community feared the loss of its long-term cohesion and economic viability. The Corps declared that it was "not authorized to run a chamber of commerce type operation to insure 'viability'." In spite of disagreements and misunderstanding on both sides, the Portland District successfully completed the $37 million relocation project, and the residents dedicated the new town in July 1978. The ultimate plan included raising the new town site above the 100-year flood plain and installing public utilities, parks, a central business district, and all public buildings for a community of 600 inhabitants—the approximate size of the original town.[5]

Field worker sifts soil to recover small or broken arifacts.

A cultural resources survey conducted during the early stages of the powerhouse project identified a significant archeological site, containing evidence in an undisturbed state of a sequence of occupations from prehistoric through historic times. The journals of explorers Lewis and Clark contained references to the Indian settlement. The site, protected under deep fill material placed during the original construction of Bonneville Dam, lay in the middle of the new river channel below the powerhouse. The Corps awarded a $1.2 million contract to recover the cultural materials necessary for site analysis and interpretation. The archeologists retrieved about 1100 cubic feet of artifacts, ranging from centuries-old stone tools and pottery to metal buttons and whisky bottles from the mid-1800s.[6]

Archeological excavation and field work at site of Bonneville second powerhouse.

Field worker plots exact position of artifact before it is removed from dig.

Other work on the project involved relocating four miles of Washington State Highway 14 and three miles of Burlington Northern's railroad track. The railroad relocation required a 1,400-foot tunnel through unstable ground, while the highway rerouting over the same terrain included three bridges and one underpass beneath the railroad. Total relocation costs came to $32 million. As finished, the project included fish facilities to pass upstream migrant adult anadromous fish and downstream migrant fingerlings. In addition, the new powerhouse contains extensive visitor facilities utilizing a self-guided tour concept. Formal dedication of the second powerhouse occurred on 1 June 1983, with the entire project reaching completion in September 1986 at a cost of $662 million.[7]

While relocation of North Bonneville and the construction of the second power-house proceeded, the Corps also investigated the need for a new navigation lock at Bonneville. The existing Bonneville Lock, completed in January 1938, was 76 feet wide and 500 feet long; while the other eight locks on Columbia-Snake Inland Waterway measured 86 feet wide by 675 feet long. As the existing annual Bonneville lock capacity of 13 million tons is reached, congestion delays will increase and the waterway capacity will be constrained. With a standard size facility, the Bonneville lock capacity would increase to 30 tons annually, adequate through the year 2040.

The smaller capacity of the Bonneville lock meant that barge tows made up for all the upstream locks must be broken into smaller units to pass through Bonneville and then reassembled for the upstream passage. This procedure doubled or tripled the time-in-system compared to the larger locks upstream. The new lock would reduce the average time-in-system from 12.7 to 1.9 hours. In addition to inadequate dimensions, the configuration of the Bonneville lock at both approaches presented hazardous conditions to shipping. The proposed size and alignment of the new lock will overcome these problems, providing safe approach conditions for large tows. The estimated construction cost of the new navigation lock project at Bonneville is $200 million, with the work slated for completion in five years (April 1992). As required by the Water Resources Development Act of 1986, 50 percent of the project funding will come from the Inland Waterways Trust Fund.[8]

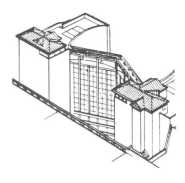

Artist's conception of new Bonneville navigation lock.

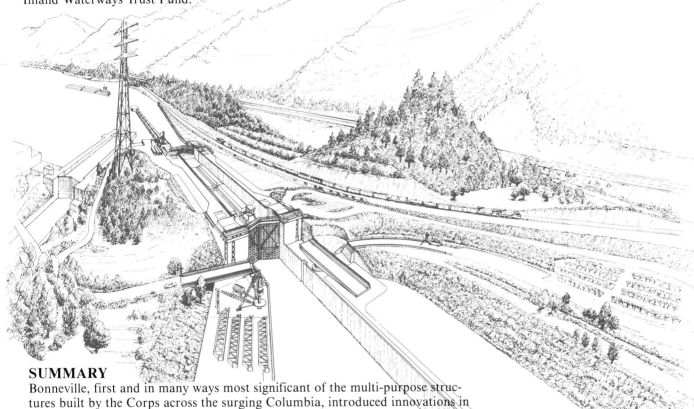

SUMMARY

Bonneville, first and in many ways most significant of the multi-purpose structures built by the Corps across the surging Columbia, introduced innovations in dam design and provided the power which would change the economic future of the Pacific Northwest. Confounding the critics who doubted that Bonneville's vast amount of hydroelectricity would ever be sold, the dam's power proved essential to the war effort and enabled the Northwest to participate in the

Second powerhouse
construction.

Cofferdam enclosing
spillway for baffle repair.

national postwar economic boom. Bonneville Dam, moreover, accomplished Roosevelt's goal of getting the Federal Government directly into the production of electric power for public and private consumers throughout the Northwest. The electrical energy from Bonneville, in turn, led directly to the creation of a Federal power marketing agency: the Bonneville Power Administration. Both undertakings fulfilled major goals of Roosevelt's New Deal for America.

At the time of its design and construction in the 1930s, the Bonneville Dam project contained many unprecedented features. No other dam in the United States had been designed to withstand floods with flows exceeding 1,000,000 cubic feet per second, as Bonneville had to do. The spillway, as a diversion/overflow structure, required a different design than the other major water impounding structures built during the 1930s, such as Roosevelt, Hoover, Shasta, and Grand Coulee dams. The original spillway design assumed that the stilling basin and baffles would require renewal at 15-year intervals. In fact, the engineers found, based on regular examinations, that both the steel and special cement used in the dam proved remarkably resistant to the effects of high-velocity water and abrasions, suffering only localized zones of erosion. The Corps did not carry out major repairs until 1955, 17 years after completion of the dam. This record justified the original decision to employ a pozzolanic cement—a judgment questioned by some experts at the time.[9]

Detail of baffle deck
showing concrete
erosion after seventeen
years.

The Bonneville powerhouse design also called for different treatment than required in other major hydroelectric projects at the time. Bonneville's planned generating capacity could be compared to only a few other hydroelectric installations and even these few operated under different design parameters. The operating "head" or pool height of Hoover, Grand Coulee, and Wilson dams remained constant, while at Bonneville considerable seasonal variation occurred. This situation led to one of the earliest major American uses of the Kaplan turbines. Other significant aspects included the massive cofferdaming effort, the innovative fish passage system, and the installation of the largest single-lift lock to that time.[10]

Planning, designing, and constructing the Bonneville project challenged the engineering and managerial capabilities of the Corps of Engineers. The North Pacific Division Commander, Colonel Thomas Robins, closely supervised the hiring and direction of the key Division and District personnel, as well as outside consultants involved in the project. Robins also played a major role in the controversial political decisions of power marketing, fish passage, and inland navigation.[11]

The public has displayed a keen interest in the Bonneville project since its inception. Hundreds of thousands annually visited during construction to observe the massive operations. This public interest has persisted over time with over 500,000 visiting the dam in 1985. Recognizing the project's role as a major regional tourist attraction, the Corps of Engineers has always operated Bonneville as a public project (except during World War II), encouraging the public to see how their tax dollars are spent. The Corps has developed two project visitor centers, containing fishviewing rooms, interpretive displays of the construction and function of the dam, and exhibits on the natural and human history of the Columbia Gorge. Similarly, the Corps has maintained much of the original character of the project, as seen in the landscaping, powerhouse, spillway, lock, fish hatchery, and administrative buildings. Reflecting the national historical significance of the Bonneville Dam project, the Secretary of the Interior has designated its remaining original elements as a National Historic Landmark. Bonneville Dam continues to fulfill the goals of its planners and builders as it contributes to the regional and national welfare.

Wind surfing on Lake Bonneville.

FOOTNOTES

Chapter 1

1. *U.S. Statutes at Large,* v. 43, pt. 1, p. 1190; U.S. Cong., *House Doc.,* No. 308, 69th Cong., 1st sess.

2. Office of the State Engineer, *Oregon's Opportunity in National Preparedness* (Salem, OR, 1916), p. 7; U.S. Dept. of the Interior, *The Story of the Columbia Basin Project,* Bureau of Reclamation (Washington, D.C., 1978), pp. 1-7; Gordon Dodds, *The American Northwest: A History of Oregon and Washington* (Arlington Heights, Il., 1986), p. 241; Fred Lockley and Marshall Dana, *"More Power To You"* (Portland, OR, 1934), pp. 63-65, 78-96, 103; Report, Col. O.E. Walsh to Division Engineer, "Revision of Civil Works Lesson No. 51" (hereafter "Civil Works Lesson"), 8 Nov. 1948, Portland District Records Holding Center (hereafter, PDRHC), pp. 2-3.

3. U.S. Cong., *House Doc.,* No. 103, 73d Cong., 1st sess.; Maj. Oscar O. Kuentz, "The Lower Columbia River Project," *Military Engineer,* XXV (Jan.-Feb., 1933), pp. 38-44; William Willingham, *Army Engineers and The Development of Oregon* (Portland, OR, 1983), pp. 93-94.

4. Col. Lukesh to Chief of Engineers, 22 Dec. 1930, National Archives Record Group 77 (hereafter, NARG 77), Records of the Chief of Engineers (hereafter, RCE), Columbia River, File No. 7249.

5. U.S. Cong., *House Doc.,* No. 103, 73d Cong., 1st sess., p. 19.

6. Ibid., p. 21.

7. Ibid., pp. 6-13.

8. Quote from *New York Times,* 22 Sept. 1932, p. 16; Richard Lowitt, *The New Deal and the West* (Bloomington, Ind., 1984), p. 160.

9. Charles Martin, "Bonneville's Beginnings," *Portland, Sunday Journal Magazine,* 30 Oct. 1949, pp. 6-7; Kimbark MacColl, *The Growth of a City (Portland, OR, 1979),* pp. 439-442; Lowitt, *The New Deal and the West,* p. 160; Gus Norwood, *Columbia River Power for the People: A History of Policies of the Bonneville Power Administration* (Washington, D.C., 1981), pp. 35-45; Chief of Engineers to Sen. Hubert Stephens, 21 Aug. 1933, NARG 77, RCE, Columbia River, File No. 7249; Chief of Engineers to Sen. Homer T. Bone, 26 Sept. 1933, ibid.; Charles Martin to Pres. Franklin Roosevelt, June 23, 1935, NARG 77, RCE, Columbia River, File No. 7249; Charles McNary to Roosevelt, Sept. 14, 1933, Library of Congress, McNary Legislative File, Bonneville (hereafter McNary Papers), Box 33; Roosevelt to McNary, 30 Sept. 1933, ibid; Steve Neal, *McNary of Oregon: A Political Biography* (Portland, OR, 1985), pp. 144-145.

10. Lockley and Dana, *"More Power To You",* pp. 67, 105-106, quote on p. 65.

11. U.S. Cong., *Senate Committee Print,* 73d Cong., 2d sess., p. 2.

12. Ibid., pp. 3-26; "Civil Works Lesson," pp. 5-9; "Progress Report, Bonneville Power-Navigation Project Federal Works Project No. 28, October 1933 to October 1934" (hereafter, "Progress Report"), PDRHC, pp. 7-10; Ira Williams, "Preliminary Geologic Report on a Series of Prospective Dam Sites on the Lower Columbia River," Aug. 1932, PDRHC, pp. 3-52; Edwin T. Hodge, "Report of Dam Sites on Lower Columbia River," Sept. 1932, PDRHC, pp. 1-81; C.P. Holdredge, "Final Geological Report on the Bonneville Project, 1937," Jan. 1937, PDRHC, pp. 1-39; U.S. Army, Corps of Engineers, "Bonneville Dam Project: History of Geological Exploration," Portland, OR, 1937, PDRHC.

13. "Progress Report," pp. 10-11; *Portland, Bonneville Dam Record,* 16 Mar. 1934, p. 1; U.S. Army, Corps of Engineers, "Bonneville Dam Project: Cofferdams and Excavation for Side Dam," Portland, OR, 1936, PDRHC.

14. Lockley and Dana, *"More Power To You",* pp. 61, 108.

Chapter 2

1. *Portland, Bonneville Dam Record,* 9 Dec. 1933, pp. 1-12, 15 Aug. 1934, pp. 4-7; "Progress Report," pp. 2-3.

2. "Progress Report," pp. 3-5, 24; U.S. Army, Corps of Engineers, *Improvement of Columbia River at Bonneville, Oregon* (Portland, OR, 1936), pp. 22-24, 29; Lee Bostwick, *Bonneville Power and Navigation Project* (Portland, OR, 1935), pp. 11, 26-27; U.S. Army, Corps of Engineers, "Bonneville Dam Project: Camp Hired Labor Forces," Portland, OR, 1936, PDRHC; *Portland, Bonneville Dam Record,* 16 Dec. 1933, p. 10, 31 Jan. 1934, pp. 1, 7, 8; U.S. Army, Corps of Engineers, "Bonneville Dam Project: Engineering Office," Portland, OR, 1936, PDRHC; U.S. Army, Corps of Engineers, Annual Reports of the Chief of Engineers, Fiscal Years 1934-1944 (Washington, D.C.: Government Printing Office, 1934-1945), 1934, Part 1, pp. 1334-1336 (hereafter, Annual Reports); Portland, *Bonneville Dam Record,* 16 Feb. 1934, p. 3, 11 July 1934, p. 8, 31 Oct. 1934, p. 5, 15 Mar. 1935, p. 6.

3. The hydraulic model studies cost $105,000 but the consulting engineer conducting them felt their contribution to the success of the entire project was worth many times that sum. Through the model studies, he wrote, "a confidence in the design has been created that could not have been established otherwise." J.C. Stevens, "A Report on Model Studies made in Connection with the Bonneville Dam." 3 vols. Portland, OR 1937, PDRHC, p. 7; "Progress Report," pp. 5-7; Corps of Engineers, *Improvement at Bonneville,* p. 22; *Portland, Bonneville Dam Record,* 18 May 1934, p. 4, 15 Dec. 1934, p. 18.

4. "Progress Report," pp. 11-12; "Civil Works Lesson," pp. 10-12; Stevens, "Model Studies," pp. 8-70; U.S. Army, Corps of Engineers, "Bonneville Dam Project:Cascade Rapids Excavation," Portland, OR, 1936, PDRHC; U.S. Army, Corps of Engineers, "Bonneville Dam Project: Channel Improvements," Portland, OR, 1936, PDRHC; C.I. Grimm, "Memorandum: Design of Main Spillway Gates," 22 Jan. 1935, PDRHC; *Portland, Bonneville Dam Record,* 6 June 1934, pp. 1, 6; Bostwick, *Bonneville Project,* pp. 14-18.

5. "Progress Report," pp. 14-16; "Civil Works Lesson," pp. 15-19; J.S. Gorlinski, "The Bonneville Dam," *Military Engineer,* XXVII (May-June 1935), p. 212; Corps of Engineers, *Improvement at Bonneville,* pp. 11-13; Bostwick, *Bonneville Project,* pp. 19-21; *Portland, Bonneville Dam Record,* 31 Jan. 1934, p. 4, 16 Feb. 1934, p. 1.

6. L.E. Kurtichanof, "Electrical Features of the Bonneville Project," paper presented at the 14th meeting of Northwest Electric Light and Power Assoc., 21-24 Apr. 1937; "Progress Report," pp. 16-17; *Portland, Bonneville Dam Record,* 16 Feb. 1934, p. 1, 28 Feb. 1934, pp. 1, 2.

7. "Progress Report," pp. 17-18; *Portland, Bonneville Dam Record,* 16 Dec. 1933, p. 3, 13 Jan. 1934, pp. 4, 5, 31 Jan. 1934, pp. 1, 3, 6, 16 Feb. 1934, pp. 3, 5, 6, 28 Feb. 1934, pp. 4, 5, 12, 16 Mar. 1934, p. 3, 14 Apr. 1934, p. 4, 18 May 1934, p. 1, 6 June 1934, pp. 2, 4, 27 June 1934, pp. 2, 4, 15 Aug. 1934, p. 1, 31 Aug. 1934, pp. 1, 6; Amedee Smith to Charles McNary, 15 Dec. 1933, McNary Papers, Box 33, McNary to Smith, ibid, McNary to C.L. Sweek, 27 Feb. 1934, ibid, McNary to A.J. Derby, 1 Mar. 1934, ibid, McNary to W.S. Nelson, 4 Apr. 1934, ibid; Inland Empire Waterways Association, Inc. "Ship Channel in Columbia River . . . Presented to the Board of Engineers for Rivers . . . May 31, 1934" (Walla Walla, Wash., 1934), PDRHC.

8. "Progress Report," p. 19; "Civil Works Lesson," pp. 21-22; Gorlinski, "The Bonneville Dam," p. 212; Theron D. Weaver, "The Columbia River between Vancouver and The Dalles," *Military Engineer,* XXXI (Mar.-Apr. 1939), pp. 92-93; Bostwick, *Bonneville Project,* pp. 21-23; Corps of Engineers, *Improvement at Bonneville,* pp. 14-17.

9. "Progress Report," p. 13; "Civil Works Lesson," pp. 13-15; Corps of Engineers, *Improvement at Bonneville,* pp. 23, 25-27; Gorlinski, "The Bonneville Dam," pp. 211-212; U.S. Army, Corps of Engineers, "Bonneville Dam Project: Main Spillway Dam, July 1934 to May 1936," 2 vols., Portland, OR, 1935-37, PDRHC; *Portland, Bonneville Dam Record,* 31 Oct. 1934, p. 1, 15 Nov. 1934, p. 4, 15 Dec. 1934, p. 5, 15 Jan 1934, p. 6, 28 Feb. 1935, p. 1, 15 Mar. 1935, p. 1.

10. Corps of Engineers, *Improvement at Bonneville,* pp. 27-28; U.S. Army, Corps of Engineers, "Bonneville Dam Project: Excavation for Lock and Powerhouse," Portland, OR, 1936, PDRHC; *Portland, Bonneville Dam Record,* 31 Jan. 1934, pp. 1, 5, 16 Feb. 1934, p. 1, 28 Feb. 1934, pp. 1-2, 3, 31 Mar. 1934, p. 10, 14 Apr. 1934, p. 2; *Bonneville Dam Chronicle,* p. 17.

11. U.S. Army, Corps of Engineers, "Bonneville Dam Project: Powerhouse and Lock Masonry and Substructure," Portland, OR, 1936, PDRHC; Corps of Engineers, *Improvement at Bonneville,* pp. 27-28; "Civil Works Lesson," p. 21; *Annual Reports, 1935,* Part 1, pp. 1512-1515; Annual Reports, 1936, Part 1, pp. 1517-1524; *Portland, Bonneville Dam Record,* 31 Aug. 1934, p. 1, 15 Dec. 1934, p. 16.

12. "Civil Works Lesson," p. 20; *Annual Reports, 1938,* Part 1, pp. 1829-1838; *Annual Reports, 1939,* Part 1, pp. 2002-2011; *Annual Reports, 1940,* Part 1, pp. 2018-2025; *Annual Reports, 1941,* Part 1, pp. 1901-1911; *Annual Reports, 1942,* Part 1, pp. 1724-1732; *Annual Reports, 1943,* Part 1, pp. 1654-1662; *Annual Reports, 1944,* Part 1, pp. 1628-1635; interview with Maj. Gen. Cecil R. Moore, 14 Oct. 1980, Office of History, Corps of Engineers.

13. "Progress Report," pp. 20-22; "Civil Works Lesson," pp. 23-25; Corps of Engineers, *Improvement at Bonneville,* pp. 20-22; Bostwick, *Bonneville Project,* pp. 23-25; U.S. Army, Corps of Engineers, "Bonneville Dam Project: Cascade Rapids Excavation," Portland, OR, 1936, PDRHC; U.S. Army, Corps of Engineers, "Bonneville Dam Project: Channel Improvements," Portland, OR, 1936, PDRHC; U.S. Army, Corps of Engineers, "History of Geological Exploration," Portland, OR, 1937, PDRHC; U.S. Army, Corps of Engineers, "Bonneville Dam Project: History of Railroad and Highway Department," Portland, OR, 1936, PDRHC; U.S. Army, Corps of Engineers, "Bonneville Dam Project: Channel Improvements Through Gorge," Portland, OR, 1936, PDRHC; *Portland, Bonneville Dam Record,* 15 Nov. 1934, p. 4, 15 Mar. 1935, p. 3.

14. Weaver, "The Columbia River," pp. 93-94; *Annual Reports, 1938,* Part 1, pp. 1840-1844; *Annual Reports, 1939,* Part 1, pp. 2002-2011; *Annual Reports, 1940,* Part 1, pp. 2026-2027; "Civil Works Lesson," p. 25.

15. R.R. Clark and H.E. Brown, "Portland-Puzzolan Cement as Used in the Bonneville Spillway Dam," *Journal of the American Concrete Institute,* XXXIII (Jan.-Feb. 1937), pp. 183-221.

16. *Ibid.;* Raymond Davis, "Cement and Concrete Investigations for Bonneville Dam," Berkeley, Calif., 1935, PDRHC; ibid., "Proposed Specifications for Portland-Puzzolan Cement for Bonneville Dam," Berkeley, Calif., 1935, PDRHC.

17. U.S. Army, Corps of Engineers, "Bonneville Dam Project:Concrete Division Operations, 1934-35," Portland, OR, 1936, PDRHC; R.R. Clark, "Memorandum: Temperature Computations—Spillway Dam Block," 13 Sept. 1935, PDRHC; U.S. Army, Corps of Engineers, "Bonneville Dam Project: Mixture Proportions and Concrete Strengths, Main Spillway Dam and Appurtenant Structures," Portland, OR, 1935, PDRHC.

18. U.S. Army, Corps of Engineers, "Bonneville Dam Project:Concrete Division Operations, 1934-35," Portland, OR, 1936, PDRHC; H.G. Gerdes, "Memorandum: Contraction Joints in Main Spillway Dam," 14 Jan. 1935, PDRHC.

19. U.S. Army, Corps of Engineers,"Bonneville Dam Project:Concrete Division Operations, 1934-35," Portland, OR, 1936, PDRHC.

20. Lois P. Myers, "Bonneville Night Scene Splendid, Awesome Sight," *Portland, The News-Telegram,* 21 Nov. 1935, pp. 1, 2.

21. U.S. Army, Corps of Engineers, "Bonneville Dam Project: Structural Section," Portland, OR, 1936, PDRHC.

22. U.S. Army, Corps of Engineers, "Bonneville Dam Project: Engineering Office," Portland, OR, 1936, PDRHC; ibid., "History of Timekeeping Department," ibid.; *Portland, Bonneville Dam Record,* 15 Aug. 1934, p. 7; *Portland, The Spillway,* 8 June 1936, p. 1.

23. *Annual Reports, 1935,* Part 1, pp. 1459, 1512; *Annual Reports, 1938,* Part 1, p. 1828; Annual Reports, 1941, Part 1, p. 1859.

24. U.S. Army, Corps of Engineers, "Bonneville Dam Project: Camp Hired Labor Forces," Portland, OR, 1936, PDRHC; *Portland, Bonneville Dam Record,* 13 Jan. 1934, p. 8, 31 Jan. 1934, pp. 7, 8; Bostwick, *Bonneville Project,* pp. 26-27.

25. U.S. Army, Corps of Engineers, "Bonneville Dam Project: Construction of Permanent Quarters," Portland, OR, 1936, PDRHC; ibid., "Permanent Roads and Landscaping," ibid.; ibid., "Auditorium and Administration Buildings," ibid.; ibid., "Walks, Curbs, Gutters, etc.," ibid.; Bostwick, *Bonneville Project,* pp. 27-28; Corps of Engineers, *Improvement at Bonneville,* p. 22; *Portland, Bonneville Dam Record,* 16 Feb. 1934, p. 11, 18 May 1934, p. 1, 15 Nov. 1934, pp. 1, 5, 15 Dec. 1934, p. 17, 15 Jan. 1935, p. 5.

26. Gen. Pillsbury to McNary, 22 June 1934, McNary Papers, Box 33; U.S. Army, Corps of Engineers, "Bonneville Dam Project: Community Center," PDRHC; ibid., "U.S. Guards," ibid.; *Portland, Bonneville Dam Record,* 31 Jan. 1934, p. 6, 27 June 1934, p. 1, 15 Aug. 1934, p. 3, 31 Aug. 1934, p. 2, 31 Oct. 1934, p. 5, 15 Dec. 1934, p. 5; Bostwick, *Bonneville Project,* pp. 26-27.

27. *Annual Reports, 1938,* Part 1, pp. 1830-1831; *Portland, Oregonian,* 29 Sept. 1937.

28. *Annual Reports, 1938,* Part 1, pp. 1830-1831; *Annual Reports, 1939,* Part 1, pp. 2003-2004, *Portland, Sunday Oregonian,* 10 July 1938.

29. J.D. Ross to Pres. Roosevelt, 31 May 1938, NARG 77, RCE, Columbia River, File No. 7249; Jim Marshall, "Dam of Doubt," *Colliers,* 19 June 1937, pp. 19, 82-84.

Chapter 3

1. Norwood, *Columbia River Power,* pp. 55-93; MacColl, *Growth of a City,* pp. 555-558; Lowitt, *The New Deal and the West,* pp. 160-163, 170-171, 227; Dodds, *The American Northwest,* pp. 228-230; W.D. Dodson to Charles McNary, 6, 16 Dec. 1933, McNary Papers, Box 33; McNary to Dodson, 7 Dec. 1933, ibid.; Gen. Pillsbury to McNary, 11 June 1937, ibid.; *Portland, Bonneville Dam Record,* 9 Dec. 1933, p. 10, 31 Jan. 1934, p. 12, 16 Jan. 1934, p. 3, 16 Mar. 1934, pp. 3, 12, 31 Oct. 1934, p. 2, 15 Nov. 1934, p. 1, 15 Dec. 1934, p. 9, 31 Dec. 1934, p. 8.

2. State Planning Board, *A Study of the Wholesale Cost of Bonneville Power* (Salem, OR, 1935), pp. 3-22; *Portland, Bonneville Dam Record,* 15 Dec. 1934, p. 20, 31 Jan. 1934, p. 8.

3. State Planning Board, *Use of Electricity in Oregon with Forecasts of Future Demands* (Salem, OR, 1936), pp. 7-48; State Planning Board, *Recommended Policies for Sale of Bonneville Power* (Salem, OR, 1936), p. 8.

4. State Planning Board, *Recommended Policies,* pp. 1-20; *Portland, Bonneville Dam Record,* 16 Mar. 1934, p. 12, 18 May 1934, p. 8.

5. Charles Martin to Pres. Roosevelt, 29 Apr. 1935, McNary Papers, Box 33; Martin to McNary, 30 Apr. 1935, ibid.; McNary to W.D. Dodson, 7 Dec. 1933, ibid.; McNary to William Woodward, 27 Feb. 1935, ibid.; Port of Portland to McNary, 30 Apr. 1935, ibid.; Dodson to McNary, 7 May 1935, ibid.; McNary to Martin, 8, 9 May 1935, ibid.; McNary to J.E. Lewton, 11 June 1935, ibid.; McNary to Ben Osborne, 21 June 1935, ibid.; McNary to William Richards, 7 Aug. 1935, ibid.; Martin to McNary, 8 May 1936, ibid., Box 34.

6. Neal, *McNary,* p. 222; Norwood, *Columbia River Power,* pp. 55-93; Lowitt, *The New Deal and the West,* pp. 160-163, 170-171.

7. Ibid.; District Engineer, United States Engineer Office, Portland, Oregon, and Bonneville Power Administrator, *The Bonneville Project* (Washington, D.C., 1941), pp. 3, 14-20.

8. Ibid.

9. Ibid.

10. Doug Soleida, "Bonneville: The War Years and Beyond," *Corps'pondent,* Apr.-May 1987, pp. 10-12.

11. "Civil Works Lesson," pp. 4, 21, 29; Marc Reisner, *Cadillac Desert* (New York, 1986), pp. 168-170.

Chapter 4   1. Col. Lukesh to Chief of Engineers, 8 Mar. 1929, NARG 77, RCE, Columbia River, File No. 7249. Some critics claim the Corps only belatedly recognized the danger Columbia River dams posed to migratory fish runs and only half-heartedly responded to the problem. See, for example, Anthony Netboy, *The Columbia River Salmon and Steelhead Trout: Their Fight for Survival* (Seattle, 1980), pp. 72-102, 145-147; Oral Bullard, Crisis on the Columbia (Portland, OR, 1968), pp. 45-46, 99-120.

2. U.S. Cong., *House Doc.,* No. 103, 73d Cong., 1st sess., pp. 10, 1539, 1597, 1599, 1602; Kuentz, "The Lower Columbia River Project," pp. 44; *Portland, Oregonian,* 1 Jan. 1934, p. 2; U.S. Cong., *Senate Doc.,* No. 87, 75th Cong. 1st sess., pp. 2, 28; Commissioner of Fisheries to Charles McNary, 9 Nov. 1933, McNary Papers, Box 33; Hugh Mitchell to McNary, 2 Aug. 1933, ibid.; quote, McNary to Mitchell, 12 Aug. 1933, ibid.; W.L. Thompson to McNary, 25 Aug. 1933, ibid.; McNary to Thompson, 28 Aug. 1933, ibid.; Frank Bell to McNary, 6 Oct. 1933, ibid.

3. "Progress Report," pp. 22-24; Commissioner of Fisheries to Charles McNary, 9 Nov. 1933, McNary Papers, Box 33; Fish Commission of the State of Oregon to Col. Thomas Robins, 5 Sept. 1934, ibid.; Fish Commission to McNary, 22 Aug. 1934, ibid.; Bostwick, *Bonneville Project,* pp. 25-26; *Portland, Bonneville Dam Record,* 28 Feb. 1934, p. 9, 11 July 1934, p. 7, 31 Aug. 1934, pp. 4-5.

4. Harlan Holmes to Anthony Netboy, 19 June 1971, copy from Public Affairs Office, Portland District, Corps of Engineers; U.S. Cong., *Senate Doc.,* No. 87, 75th Cong., 1st sess., pp. 29-39, quote p. 29; Fish Commission of the State of Oregon to Col. Thomas Robins, 5 Sept. 1934, McNary Papers, Box 33; Report, "Public Hearings on Adequate Fishways at Bonneville Dam," Portland District, Corps of Engineers, McNary Papers, Box 33, quote on p. 98; Holmes, in a letter to W.D.B. Dodson of the Portland Chamber of Commerce, summed up the commitment to save the migratory fish runs: "I should not hesitate to state that there can be no basis for any public opinion to the effect that there is a deliberate and thoughtless destruction of the Columbia River salmon industry. All interested State and Federal departments are aware of the importance of the problem and conscientiously endeavored to provide what they consider to be proper and adequate means of fish protection." 13 Nov. 1935, McNary Papers, Box 34.

5. Charles McNary to John Veatch, 14 Sept. 1934, 7 Jan. 1935, 1 Feb. 1935, 6 Mar. 1935, 12 Mar. 1935, McNary Papers, Box 34; Veatch to McNary, 22 Sept. 1934, 2 Feb. 1935, 12 Mar. 1935, ibid.; Hugh Mitchell to McNary, 4 Oct. 1934, ibid.; Astoria Chamber of Commerce to McNary, 24 Nov. 1934, ibid.; Oregon State Game Commission to McNary, 21 Dec. 1934, ibid.; McNary to Ralph Cowgill, 27 Dec. 1934, 21 Feb. 1935, 6 Mar. 1935, 12 Mar. 1935, ibid.; Cowgill to McNary, 19 Feb. 1935, 12 Mar. 1935, ibid.; Gen. Markham to McNary, 10 Jan. 1935, 2 Feb. 1935, 19 Feb. 1935, 27 Feb. 1935, 22 May 1935, ibid.; McNary to Markham, 21 Feb. 1935, ibid.; *Portland, Bonneville Dam Record,* 15 Dec. 1934, p. 2, 31 Dec. 1934, p. 3, 31 Jan. 1935, p. 5, 15 Feb. 1935, pp. 1, 7, 8, 15 Mar. 1935, pp. 1, 8.

6. John Veatch to Charles McNary, 6 June 1935, Charles McNary Papers, Box 34; Fish Commission to McNary, 22 Mar. 1935, ibid.

7. The following description of facilities is based on Gorlinski, "The Bonneville Dam," p. 213; U.S. Cong., *Senate Doc.,* No. 87, 75th Cong., 1st sess., pp. 29-43; Corps of Engineers, *Improvement of the Columbia River,* pp. 18-20; U.S. Army, Corps of Engineers, *Power, Navigation and Fish Facilities on the Columbia River at Bonneville Dam* (Portland, OR, 1948), pp. 18-22; Netboy, *Columbia River Salmon,* pp. 76-78; Harlan Holmes, "The Passage of Fish at Bonneville Dam," Department of Research, Oregon Fish Commission, *Contribution No. 2* (1940), pp. 182-186; "Fishways at Bonneville," *Engineering News-Record,* 116 (13 Feb. 1936), pp. 236-238; Frank T. Bell, "Guarding the Columbia's Silver Horde," *Nature Magazine,* 29 (Jan. 1939), pp. 43-47.

8. U.S. Cong., *Senate Doc.,* No. 87, 75th Cong., 1st sess., p. 30.

9. Corps of Engineers, *Power, Navigation and Fish Facilities,* pp. 21-22.

10. U.S. Cong., *Senate Doc.,* No. 87, 75th Cong., 1st sess., p. 43; Holmes, "The Passage of Fish," p. 186; *Annual Reports, 1938,* Part 1, p. 1831; Netboy, *Columbia River Salmon,* pp. 77-78. See also, U.S. Dept. of Interior, Memorandum for the Press: Bonneville Project, 19 June 1938, McNary Papers, Box 37.

11. Stephen Beckham, *The Bonneville Hatchery: A Historical Assessment for the Bonneville Navigation Lock Project, Bonneville, Oregon* (Eugene, OR, 1986), pp. 1-35.

12. Ibid., pp. 27-33; U.S. Army, Corps of Engineers, "Bonneville Dam Project: History of Railroad and Highway Department," Portland, OR, 1936, PDRHC; *Portland, Bonneville Dam Record,* 31 Oct. 1934, p. 5.

13. Ed Chaney and L. Edward Perry, *Columbia Basin Salmon and Steelhead Analysis: Summary Report, September 1, 1976* (Portland, OR, 1976), pp. 6-7; Northwest Power Planning Council, *Compilation of Information on Salmon and Steelhead Losses in the Columbia River Basin* (Portland, OR, 1986), pp. 76-95, 128-158.

14. Willingham, *Army Engineers and the Development of Oregon,* pp. 197-202; Northwest Power Planning Council, *Compilation on Salmon and Steelhead Losses,* pp. 213, 224-225.

15. Charles Koski, et al., *Fish Transportation Oversight Team Annual Report — FY 1986, Transport Operations on the Snake and Columbia Rivers* (Portland, OR, 1987), pp. 2-60; R. Gregory Nokes, "Salmon Run Recovers after 50-year Upriver Fight," *Portland, Oregonian,* 14 June 1987, pp. 1, C6.

16. U.S. Army, Corps of Engineers, *Bonneville Second Powerhouse* (Portland, OR, 1984), p. 5; U.S. Army, Corps of Engineers, *2nd Powerhouse Fish Facilities Design Memorandum No. 9* (Portland, OR, 1974); ibid., *Supplement No. 5* (Portland, OR, 1980).

Chapter 5   1. Willingham, *Army Engineers and the Development of Oregon,* pp. 220-221.
2. Corps of Engineers, *Bonneville Second Powerhouse,* p. 8.
3. Ibid., U.S. Army, Corps of Engineers, *2nd Powerhouse Preliminary Design Report No. 11* (Portland, OR, 1975); ibid., *2nd Powerhouse General Design Memorandum No. 4 Supplement No. 3 Turbine Study* (Portland, OR, 1974-1975); ibid., *General Design Memorandum No. 4* (Portland, OR, 1972).
4. Corps of Engineers, *Bonneville Second Powerhouse,* pp. 3-5.
5. Ibid., p. 4; Willingham, *Army Engineers and the Development of Oregon,* pp. 221-223.
6. Rick Minor, et al., *An Overview of Investigation at 45SA11: Archaeology in the Columbia River Gorge* (Eugene, OR, 1986).
7. Corps of Engineers, *Bonneville Second Powerhouse,* pp. 5-6.
8. U.S. Army, Corps of Engineers, "Information Paper: Bonneville Navigation Lock" (Portland, OR, 3 Mar. 1987).
9. C.C. Galbraith and R.R. Clark, "Bonneville Dam Concrete after Six Years," *Engineering News-Record* (8 Mar. 1945), pp. 121-124; R.R. Clark, "Effects of High-Velocity Water on Bonneville Dam Concrete," *Journal of the American Concrete Institute* (June 1950), pp. 821-839; ibid., "Bonneville Dam Stilling Basin Repaired after 17 Years Service," *Journal of the American Concrete Institute* (Apr. 1956), pp. 822-837.
10. Donald Jackson to William Willingham, 23 Apr. 1987, personal communication.
11. *Oregon, Daily Journal,* 1 Aug. 1934; *Portland, Bonneville Dam Record,* 11 July 1934, p. 6, 31 Oct. 1934, p. 8, 15 Nov. 1934, pp. 1, 5; George Sandy to Charles McNary, 15 July 1933, McNary Papers, Box 33.

BIBLIOGRAPHY

Monographs

Beckham, Stephen. The Bonneville Hatchery: *A Historical Assessment for the Bonneville Navigation Lock Project, Bonneville, Oregon.* Eugene: Heritage Research Associates, 1986.

Bonneville Dam Chronicle. Portland: The Dam Chronicle, n.d.

Bostwick, Lee. *Bonneville Power and Navigation Project.* Portland: Columbian Press, Inc., 1935.

Bullard, Oral. *Crisis on the Columbia.* Portland: Touchstone Press, 1968.

Chaney, Ed and Perry, L. Edward. *Columbia Basin Salmon and Steelhead Analysis: Summary Report, September 1, 1976.* Portland: n.p., 1976.

Dodds, Gordon B. *The American Northwest: A History of Oregon and Washington.* Arlington Heights: The Forum Press, Inc., 1986.

Lockley, Fred and Dana, Marshall. "More Power To You". Portland: The Oregon Journal, 1934.

Lowitt, Richard. *The New Deal and the West.* Bloomington: Indiana University Press, 1984.

MacColl, Kimbark. *The Growth of a City.* Portland: Georgian Press, 1979.

Minor, Rick, et al. *An Overview of Investigation at 45SA11: Archaeology in the Columbia River Gorge.* Eugene: Heritage Research Associates, 1986.

Neal, Steve. *McNary of Oregon: A Political Biography.* Portland: Western Imprints, 1985.

Netboy, Anthony. *The Columbia River Salmon and Steelhead Trout: Their Fight for Survival.* Seattle: University of Washington, 1980.

Norwood, Gus. *Columbia River Power for the People: A History of Policies of the Bonneville Power Administration.* Washington: n.p., 1981.

Reisner, Marc. *Cadillac Desert: The American West and Its Disappearing Water.* New York: Viking Penguin Inc., 1963.

Willingham, William. *Army Engineers and the Development of Oregon.* Portland, OR: U.S. Army Engineer District, 1983.

Periodicals

Bell, Frank T. "Guarding the Columbia's Silver Horde." *Nature Magazine,* 29 (Jan. 1939).

Clark, R.R. "Bonneville Dam Stilling Basin Repaired after 17 Years Service." *Journal of the American Concrete Institute,* April 1956.

Clark, R.R. "Effects of High-Velocity Water on Bonneville Dam Concrete." *Journal of the American Concrete Institute,* June 1950.

Clark, R.R. and Brown, H.E. "Portland-Puzzolan Cement as Used in the Bonneville Spillway Dam." *Journal of the American Concrete Institute,* XXXIII (January-February 1937).

"Fishways at Bonneville." *Engineering News-Record,* 116 (13 February 1936).

Galbraith, C.C. and Clark, R.R. "Bonneville Dam Concrete after Six Years." Engineering News-Record, 8 March 1945.

Gorlinski, J.S. "The Bonneville Dam." *Military Engineer,* XXVI (May-June 1935).

Holmes, Harlan. "The Passage of Fish at Bonneville Dam," Department of Research, Oregon Fish Commission, *Contribution No. 2,* 1940.

Kuentz, Major Oscar O. "The Lower Columbia River Project." *Military Engineer,* XXV (January-February 1933).

Marshall, Jim. "Dam of Doubt." Colliers, 19 June 1937.

Martin, Charles. "Bonneville's Beginnings." *Portland, Sunday Journal Magazine,* 30 October 1949.

Myers, Lois P. "Bonneville Night Scene Splendid, Awesome Sight." *Portland, The News-Telegram,* 21 November 1935.

New York Times, 22 September 1932.

Nokes, R. Gregory. "Salmon Run Recovers after 50-year Upriver Fight." *Portland, Oregonian,* 14 June 1987.

Portland, Bonneville Dam Record, 9, 16 December 1933; 13, 16, 31 January; 16, 28 February; 16, 31 March; 14 April; 18 May; 6, 27 June; 11 July; 15, 31 August; 31 October; 15 November; 15, 31 December 1934; 15, 31 January; 15 February; 15 March 1935.

Portland, Oregon Daily Journal, 1 August 1984.

Portland, Oregonian, 1 January 1934; 29 September 1937; 10 July 1938.

Portland, The Spillway, 8 June 1936.

Soleida, Doug. "Bonneville: The War Years and Beyond." *Corps'pondent,* April-May 1987, pp. 10-12.

Weaver, Theron D. "The Columbia River between Vancouver and The Dalles." *Military Engineer,* XXXI (March-April 1939).

Government Documents

U.S. Congress. *House Document,* Number 103, 73d Congress, 1st Session, 1932-1934.

U.S. Congress. *House Document,* Number 308, 69th Congress, 1st Session, 1926.

U.S. Congress. *Senate Committee Print,* 73d Congress, 2d Session, 1934.

U.S. Congress. *Senate Document,* Number 87, 75th Congress, 1st Session, 1938.

District Engineer, United States Engineer Office, Portland, Oregon, and Bonneville Power Administrator. *The Bonneville Project.* Washington: U.S. Government Printing Office, 1941.

Office of the State Engineer. *Oregon's Opportunity in National Preparedness.* Salem: State of Oregon, 1916.

U.S. Army. Corps of Engineers. *Annual Reports of the Chief of Engineers, Fiscal Years 1934-1944.* Washington, D.C.: Government Printing Office, 1934-1945.

————. *Bonneville Second Powerhouse.* Portland: U.S. Army Engineer District, 1984.

————. *General Design Memorandum No. 4.* Portland: U.S. Army Engineer District, 1972.

—————. *Improvement of Columbia River at Bonneville, Oregon.* Portland: U.S. Army Engineer District, 1936.

—————. "Information Paper: Bonneville Navigation Lock." Portland: U.S. Army Engineer District, 1986.

—————. *Power, Navigation and Fish Facilities on the Columbia River at Bonneville Dam.* Portland: U.S. Army Engineer District, 1948.

—————. *2nd Powerhouse Fish Facilities Design Memorandum No. 9.* Portland: U.S. Army Engineer District, 1974.

—————. *2nd Powerhouse Fish Facilities Design Memorandum Supplement No. 2.* Portland: U.S. Army Engineer District, 1974.

—————. *2nd Powerhouse General Design Memorandum No. 4 Supplement No. 3 Turbine Study.* Portland: U.S. Army Engineer District, 1974-1975.

—————. *2nd Powerhouse Preliminary Design Report No. 11.* Portland: U.S. Army Engineer District, 1975.

Portland, Oregon. Portland District Record Holding Center.

Clark. R.R. "Memorandum: Temperature Computation — Spillway Dam Block," 13 September 1935.

Davis, Raymond. "Cement and Concrete Investigations for Bonneville Dam," Berkeley, 1935.

Grimm, C.I. "Memorandum: Design of Main Spillway Gates," 22 January 1935.

Hodge, Edwin T. "Report of Dam Sites on Lower Columbia River," September 1932. Holdredge, C.P. "Final Geological Report on the Bonneville Project, 1937," January 1937.

Inland Empires Waterway Association, Inc. "Ship Channel in Columbia River. . . Presented to Board of Engineers for Rivers . . . May 31, 1934," Walla Walla, 1934.

Kurtichanof, L.E. "Electrical Features of the Bonneville Project," Paper presented at the 14th meeting of Northwest Electric Light and Power Association, 21-24 April 1937.

"Progress Report, Bonneville Power — Navigation Project Federal Works Project No. 28, October 1933 to October 1934."

"Proposed Specifications for Portland-Puzzolan Cement for Bonneville Dam," Berkeley, 1935.

Report. Colonel O.E. Walsh to Division Engineer. "Revision of Civil Works Lesson No. 51," 8 November 1948.

Stevens, J.C. "A Report on Model Studies made in Connection with the Bonneville Dam," 3 volumes. Portland, Oregon, U.S. Army Engineer District, 1937.

U.S. Army. Corps of Engineers. "Bonneville Dam Project: Auditorium and Administration Buildings," Portland, Oregon: U.S. Army Engineer District, 1936.

————. "Bonneville Dam Project: Camp Hired Labor Forces," Portland, Oregon: U.S. Army Engineer District, 1936.

————. "Bonneville Dam Project: Cascade Rapids Excavation," Portland, Oregon: U.S. Army Engineer District, 1936.

————. "Bonneville Dam Project: Channel Improvements," Portland, Oregon: U.S. Army Engineer District, 1936

————. "Bonneville Dam Project: Channel Improvements Through Gorge," Portland, Oregon: U.S. Army Engineer District, 1936.

————. "Bonneville Dam Project: Cofferdams and Excavation for Side Dam," Portland, Oregon: U.S. Army Engineer District, 1936.

————. "Bonneville Dam Project: Concrete Division Operations, 1934-1935," Portland, Oregon: U.S. Army Engineer District, 1936.

————. "Bonneville Dam Project: Community Center."

————. "Bonneville Dam Project: Construction of Permanent Quarters," Portland, Oregon: U.S. Army Engineer District, 1936.

————. "Bonneville Dam Project: Engineering Office," Portland, Oregon: U.S. Army Engineer District, 1936.

————. "Bonneville Dam Project: Excavation for Lock and Powerhouse," Portland, Oregon: U.S. Army Engineer District, 1936.

————. "Bonneville Dam Project: History of Railroad and Highway Department," Portland, Oregon: U.S. Army Engineer District, 1936.

————. "Bonneville Dam Project: History of Timekeeping Department," Portland, Oregon: U.S. Army Engineer District, 1936.

————. "Bonneville Dam Project: Main Spillway Dam, July 1934 to May 1936," 2 volumes. Portland, Oregon: U.S. Army Engineer District, 1935-1937.

————. "Bonneville Dam Project: Mixture Proportions and Concrete Strengths, Main Spillway Dam and Appurtenant Structures," Portland, Oregon: U.S. Army Engineer District, 1935.

————. "Bonneville Dam Project: Permanent Roads and Landscaping," Portland, Oregon: U.S. Army Engineer District, 1936.

————. "Bonneville Dam Project: Powerhouse and Lock Masonry and Substructure," Portland, Oregon: U.S. Army Engineer District, 1935.

————. "Bonneville Dam Project: Structural Section," Portland, Oregon: U.S. Army Engineer District, 1936.

————. "Bonneville Dam Project: U.S. Guards."

————. "Bonneville Dam Project: Walks, Curbs, Gutters, etc." Portland, Oregon: U.S. Army Engineer District, 1936.

Williams, Ira. "Preliminary Geologic Report on a Series of Prospective Dam Sites on the Lower Columbia River," August 1932.

Washington, D.C., National Archives. Record Group 77.

Koski, Charles, et al. *Fish Transportation Oversight Team Annual Report — FY 1986. Transport Operations on the Snake and Columbia Rivers.* Portland: National Oceanic and Atmospheric Administration, 1987.

Northwest Power Planning Council. *Compilation on Salmon and Steelhead Losses in the Columbia River Basin.* Portland: Northwest Power Planning Council, 1986.

State Planning Board. *A Study of the Wholesale Cost of Bonneville Power.* Salem: State of Oregon, 1935.

State Planning Board. *Recommended Policies for Sale of Bonneville Power.* Salem: State of Oregon, 1936.

State Planning Board. *Use of Electricity in Oregon with Forecasts of Future Demands.* Salem: State of Oregon, 1936.

U.S. Department of Interior. *The Story of the Columbia Basin Project.* Bureau of Reclamation. Washington: U.S. Government Printing Office, 1978.

U.S. Statutes at Large, v. 43, pt. 1. Washington: U.S. Government Printing Office, 1924-1925.

Interviews and Personal Communications

Holmes, Harlan to Anthony Netboy. 19 June 1971. Public Affairs Office, Portland District, Corps of Engineers.

Jackson, Donald to William Willingham, 23 April 1987.

Moore, Major General Cecil R. Interviewed by Office of History. Washington, D.C. 14 October 1980.

Manuscript Collections

Washington, D.C. Library of Congress. McNary Legislative File.

NOTE ABOUT THE AUTHOR

William F. Willingham serves as Portland District Historian and teaches early American history part-time at Lewis and Clark College. He graduated from Willamette University (1966) and earned his Ph.D. in history at Northwest University (1972). His previous writings include *Eliphalet Dyer, Connecticut Revolutionary* (1977), *Army Engineers and the Development of Oregon* (1983), *Enlightenment Science in the Pacific Northwest: The Lewis and Clark Expedition* (ed., 1984), and numerous scholarly articles and reviews.